5-

How to Build Your Dream Home

Without Getting Nailed!

Save Your Time, Money,

Sanity and Relationships

By: The Chubby Builder

ISBN - 978-0-692-35657-9 for Print Copy

Copyright page and acknowledgments are at the end of the book.

If you enjoy reading this book and learn something from it, I hope you will consider giving me a good review on Amazon.com. If you don't I hope you will contact me with suggestions to make it better. Please contact me if you have any questions.

The Chubby Builder

http://chubbybuilder.com

chubby@chubbybuilder.com

(J)

(K)

(L)

(M)

(N)

(O)

(P)

(Q)

(R)

(S)

(T)

(U)

(V)

(W)

(X)

(Y)

(Z)

Don't Worry, Be Happy

"If you treat every situation as a life and death matter, you'll die a lot of times". ~Dean Smith

Dean Smith was a legendary University of North Carolina basketball coach. His words will serve you well if you keep the above quote in mind while building your dream home. Homebuilding is a process, and like any process there will be ups and downs, good and bad. Keep in mind that it wlll all work out. Very few mistakes can't be fixed and no house will ever be perfect.

This book is short and to the point on purpose. You and I are both too busy to intentionally fill it with fluff just to make it a certain length. It would be boring and it would deplete the value for you. I have written in both conversational and storytelling styles, often called "creative non-fiction", in an effort to make it a more interesting read. As you read the stories, the lessons I have learned are embedded in a way that hopefully will make it easier for you to avoid the same mistakes.

I built my first house in 1994 and became a full time licensed builder in 1998. Since then I have built dozens of homes and completed more than 40 remodels. As a company we have built houses mostly as spec (built to sell) but have also built many custom homes for customers, on their own land. We have built homes by nearly every method available from traditional stick framing, to modular, to metal framed, to panelized and to every method in between (explained later). I have built using all brick, brick and stone, vinyl etc. You name it, we have used it. Most importantly, I have both made and lost money on houses. Therefore, I am about as qualified as anyone to write a book like this one.

I decided to write this book a couple of years ago after an experience that turned out to be a nightmare for all involved. It started out fine with me being recommended by a friend of a friend. I also knew up front that the customers were going to be difficult from day one. Against my better judgment and experience, I changed well founded rules and procedures to accommodate the customers mainly because I wanted to repay the friends who had recommended me.

This experience is shared in a later chapter but suffice it to say, the lessons I learned on this one event will last me a lifetime. The experience made me realize there had to be a better way. The customers were retiring and building their first custom dream home. It should have been a great experience for them and for me. However it all went to hell in a hand basket.

I realized, much too late, everything that went wrong was my fault. Not because I had cut corners, had done anything intentionally wrong or did not know what I was doing; but because I failed to properly educate my customer about how the whole process worked. I was so intent on giving the customers their way, to please them with little things, that I forgot the big picture of what would make everyone the happiest in the end.

In this book, I hope to show you what to do and what not to do in homebuilding. You can make the process the enjoyable experience it can and should be. Most people never get to experience seeing their home go from an empty lot to a place they always dreamed of: yet many of us that do end up feeling that the whole process was a nightmare. Some married couples end up in divorce court and never move into the home they worked so hard for. All of that is a shame. It shouldn't be that way.

What this book does <u>not</u> do is show you how to be your own contractor. Most people don't have the time to take on such a complicated and time consuming project. There have been many books written on that subject and no matter what they tell you, it's not easy. You will <u>not</u> save the huge amounts of money they often claim. Think about it for a moment. Is a supplier going to sell you his products for your one house anywhere near what a builder, who builds several houses a year, can purchase supplies for in bulk? Is a subcontractor going to consider your solo project a priority over a job for a contractor that employs them regularly?

On one of my first projects a framer who had a pretty solid reputation, pulled off my job to go do a project for a builder for whom they framed several houses per year. Fortunately I had enough of a crew and the expertise to be able to finish the work but it could have been a real mess. Subcontractors rarely are willing to finish another subs work and if they do, it will be very profitable for them. So this book will teach you how to work with a contractor, to make sure you get what you pay for, and to enjoy the process while building your dream home.

It is my goal to help anyone who follows the advice in this book to come away from the homebuilding process feeling it was one of the most exciting and pleasant experiences of their life. That's the way homebuilding should be for you; because after all, for most people it is often a once in a lifetime experience.

Thank you for purchasing this book. I hope you enjoy reading it as much as I enjoyed writing it.

Chubby Builder

Advantages and Pitfalls of Building a Custom Home

The ability to make all the decisions when building a home can be a double edged sword. On the one hand you get what you ask for and on the other hand, you get what you ask for. At times, it can be better to not have too many choices. When folks go over budget, it's often the result of too many choices. While there are drawbacks, in my opinion the advantages outweigh the disadvantages.

Advantages:

The most obvious advantage in building a house is you get exactly what you think you want in your new home. I say what you think you want because as anyone who has ever built a custom home knows, you would always change something if you had it to do over.

You get to pick out the exact location of your new dream home. Not only do you get to pick out the general location, you can pretty much pick out the exact location. You decide the where the sun enters your house, the views, the length of your driveway and any other consideration location entails.

You pick the design, the look, and the feel of both the interior and exterior. You have input into the quality of the products and materials that go into the home. You control the quality of workmanship and you decide what materials will be used. Want brick? You win. Do you want purple walls with pink trim? Yep, you win again. Of course this assumes you can pay for it, and you're willing to live with the consequences of purple walls and pink trim.

You have the chance to consider possible future life changes and plan for these changes from the start. For example, you know you plan to stay in this home for the rest of your life. You can put in features that will make future modifications work. You may know that an aging parent will probably move in one day. When we built our present home we designed two master suites so my Mom would feel more at home. You can consider what features would help or hurt future resale value and make decisions accordingly. For example, if you know it is a possibility that you may one day be transferred to another city, do you really want to buy that $10,000 built in refrigerator?

You can customize the utilities to save money or build a greener home. Most pre-existing homes don't have modern appliances like tank-less water heaters, super-efficient HVAC units, or the latest water purifiers. With a custom home these advantages can be designed without the difficulties of adding them later.

Custom construction takes advantage of the latest design trends. It's doubtful you'll pick a split-foyer with aluminum casement windows, green appliances and pink carpet when you have other choices. Remember the 70's?

You're protected from unexpected costs with a new home warranty. Modern homes can be warrantied for up to 10 years at a very reasonable cost. Even with a detailed inspection, existing homes typically have some hidden surprises somewhere.

Everything in the home can be customized to fit your needs. Have 15 television sets? The cable or satellite drops, phone jacks, and electrical outlets can be set to accommodate your every need. Have 6 dogs, 3 cats, a frog and a pot-bellied pig? You can design in features to please them too.

You are able to include upgrades into your original mortgage, making the financial impact less painful because the cost of the extras will be spread out over the life of the mortgage. You will see first-hand how the home is constructed, the placement of load bearing walls, placement of utility inlets and other information that will come in handy if you make future modifications.

If you bothered to purchase this book you have probably already decided to build a custom home. But it's always a good idea to look at both sides of any issue. Considering the disadvantages also will help you to be aware of issues you need to avoid.

Disadvantages

Without discipline, costs can rise well above budget. Little upgrades here and there seem so harmless but they add up real quick. I've seen these little extras add up to thousands of dollars and unless the client either had deep pockets or an understanding banker, the situation would end up sucking in a hurry.

Financing a custom home can be challenging because of the inherent uncertainty of new construction. No matter how much we all try to avoid surprises they're going to happen. We always do our best to anticipate and prepare for problems but, like life, homebuilding can be uncertain.

Banks recognize this so they tend to prefer loans on existing homes.

There can be unexpected costs that, for the most part, cannot be detected ahead of time without expensive testing. I've seen unexpected rock discoveries add $30,000 and more to construction costs. Although it's rare they would run that high, it can and does happen.

The unique products and features that are essential to you may not be of value to the general market at resale time. This can make it difficult to recover the cost of certain upgrades. For example, while high end appliances and solid countertops like granite add to the appeal of a home, a potential buyer is rarely willing to pay the full value of these upgrades. Custom homes with lots of upgrades often don't sell for full asking price and designs that reflect your unique tastes may not appeal to a wider audience.

If building in a time of higher material prices, custom homes can be substantially higher than an existing home. Obviously custom homes take time to build, whereas an existing home can usually be occupied in 30 days or less. After Hurricane Katrina building materials like OSB, plywood, and shingles doubled and sometimes tripled overnight.

Building a custom home is a reasonably complicated process requiring hundreds of decisions. Situations often arise that are no big deal for an experienced builder but can seem devastating to you. The tendency is furniture and other decorative items, while fine in your previous home, will be "too ugly" or somehow unacceptable in the new home. When we moved into our present home the couch didn't match, we suddenly needed a formal dining room set, and of course the TV wasn't big enough.

It is much easier to negotiate the price of an existing home. With custom building the costs are what they are. The lumber supplier doesn't care that 2x4s were only $0.35 when the home you're looking at was built. You miss out on the volume pricing that is available when purchasing a new track or semi-custom home from a builder. The biggest cost advantage of buying a new home from a "production builder" versus building custom is this volume pricing.

Some areas intentionally make new construction difficult with impact fees, ridiculous regulations and requirements that can add costs to the building process. The "geniuses" on our county commission implemented a $1.00 per square foot impact fee on all new construction effective in January 2009, after the "great recession" had been raging for over a year. To illustrate, before you even broke ground on a 2,000 square foot home you were forced to pay $2,000 plus the cost of a building permit with no added value. This action effectively shut down home building in our county from 2009-2013.

Of course this list of advantages and disadvantages is not 100% complete but hopefully you get the picture.

Chapter 1

Location, Location, Location!

"There are three things that matter in real estate location, location and location." ~ Lord Harold Samuel, British Real Estate Tycoon.

According to British Real Estate Tycoon Lord Samuel, location is so important to the value of any piece of real estate that everything else pales in comparison. While you may already have a lot or piece of land to build on; there are still many things to consider about the property before breaking ground. If you have yet to buy a building site, the following will be especially helpful to you.

Over the years I have made my share of mistakes buying lots to build spec homes. As painful as those mistakes were, the mistakes made by custom home clients (who should have known better) always seemed to cause me the most pain. I say they should have known better because I told them up front about potential problems that they did not want to hear. It seemed that no matter how intelligent, successful or frugal the clients were, they always had to learn the hard way. Just like my grandkids, they rarely listened and usually blamed me when the chickens came home to roost. I tell you this now with the fervent hope that when someone reveals critical information that you really do not want to hear, **YOU WILL LISTEN AND CONSIDER WHAT THEY SAY VERY CAREFULLY.**

Successful Location Decision Making

Sometimes I only find out where I should be going by going somewhere I didn't want to be. - Buckminster Fuller

---

It never ceases to amaze me how otherwise sane, intelligent people can become completely Irrational morons when they start to build a house. I have to admit though, early in my career I made some of the same mistakes when I built spec homes. In fact, many new builders get in trouble because they make decisions based on their own feelings or beliefs about what the market wants or what is essential in a new home. Basing key decisions on feelings or opinions without careful consideration of the facts has cost many builders and homeowners dearly.

With that in mind the first thing one **must do** before starting a new home is decide what is **really important** to everyone in the family. In essence, you need to sit down and make a detailed list of every feature in every room of your new home. You need to look at each item and flesh out everyone's true reason for wanting an item included. Will this feature really make a difference? Will the feature mean anything 5 or 10 years from now and will you get enough utility or enjoyment from it to justify the cost?

No decision you make about your new home will have a bigger influence on your total satisfaction than location. I don't just mean what part of town your property is in but many factors that some folks never really consider. Following is a short discussion of some of the most important things to consider when choosing a location. Now before you say "well duh" about some of these things, and you will, make sure you have a clear understanding of the consequences of each item discussed. Like my Dad used to say, every decision has consequences. They may be good or bad but consequences always have some effect.

- The first thing to consider on location is you cannot change it. I have seen people fall in love with a lot, buy it, and then regret it later. A poor lot selection process will echo negatively throughout the rest of the project.
- Pay close attention to the areas that surround a location. I know a developer who developed a beautiful subdivision in an older part of a small town. The lots and the spec homes sold well for the first few years. The back of the property bordered on the outskirts of a high crime area with rundown conditions. He went to great expense to build a wall separating the two areas but as the residents of the older area passed away, the blighted area just seemed to start surrounding the subdivision. When an economic downturn began, the developer went broke and the homeowners could not sell their homes. It was bad for everyone.
- Look at the makeup of the types of homeowners in the immediate area. Will your lifestyle be comparable to those around you? If you are retiring you may not be happy in a neighborhood

dominated by families with young kids and vice-versa.

- Pay special attention to the size, price and age of the homes surrounding you. Before the big downturn in 2008 many people were going into older neighborhoods with smaller homes and building much larger houses often dubbed" McMansions" by their neighbors. The surrounding homes were often more than 30 years old and could be sold at a profit for a fraction of what the "McMansion" would need to sell for. Believe me; you do not want to try selling in an area where your home is priced many times higher than the homes around you.
- Listen to your instincts. Do not ignore or gloss over conditions that you or your advisors suspect may be a problem later. The view on top of that ridge may be wonderful but if there are large outcroppings of exposed rock, you could be in for some very depressing surprises.
- Try talking to the landowners bordering your prospective property. I once built a home for a client on a lot that had been filled with loose un-compacted soil. All the neighbors had watched as the developer did the fill work. Had my client just paid a quick visit to his future neighbors he most likely would have found out about the soil conditions and saved himself thousands of dollars.
- When looking at a property ask the owner or developer if there has been any fill work done and if so where. They can't lie about it without being liable in the future. Have it stated in the contract

that to the best of their knowledge no fill work had been performed where it would matter (like under your new home).

- Don't fall in love so much with a property that you kid yourself into thinking it will be ok. The client I mentioned above refused to confront the developer when we ran into trouble. The entire right rear corner of the $400,000 home had to be built over fill that went down more than six feet. In order to remedy the situation we had to excavate two thirds of the house, digging down more than six feet to fill the entire area with compacted stone. I strongly urged him to make the developer either trade the lot out or pay the additional costs, but his response was he and his wife really loved the lot. In the end the decision cost him several thousand dollars he could not afford. Of course he later got mad and blamed me saying I had not properly estimated the cost of excavation.
- On the same note, when I developed my first large property, we were excavating the streets and encountered a large burn pit that had to be excavated and filled with compacted stone. A burn pit is an area where an excavator will dig a large hole in the ground and fill it with trees to be burned. After burning the trees they will fill the pit back in with loose soil creating an area with very unstable soil. I made the seller show us where additional pits were, share the cost of fixing the problem, and sign an affidavit stating there were no more burn pits on the property. I still wake up

sometimes in a cold sweat having dreamed about a big sink hole forming.

- Be sure to consider proximity to desirable things like good schools, hospitals, shopping, restaurants, etc. While you may not be concerned with those features your future prospective buyers may very well be.
- Look carefully at the terrain of the land you are considering. Will the home design you are planning fit on the lot? Can the home be placed where a basement can be dug? Are the slopes in the direction suitable for an open walk-in basement? Does the natural water flow run water onto your land or from your land to someone else's property? Is there an easy way to route water where it needs to go?

In today's world you have to be very careful not to buy land with environmental issues. A low spot on your land with certain types of plants may be deemed wetlands. We once developed a piece of commercial property with less than an acre of low woodlands in Florida. It was nothing more than a small area, with a few trees, where water flowed after a heavy rain. The Southwest Florida Water Management District (commonly referred to as swiftmud) decided that the area was a wetland. $70,000 later, with $15,000 of that going to swiftmud, we got our permit to build.

But WE Love This Lot

After hours of digging in the same spot, with the bucket on the backhoe going deeper and deeper, we realized we had a problem. Up until this point, digging the footings for this 2,200 square foot basement had gone smoothly. We were ahead of schedule. Now in the back right corner of the house we had come to a complete standstill.

The backhoe operator Billy shut down the machine and said, "Hey Chub, I'm down more than six feet in this one spot and I haven't hit solid ground yet."

"Great, can you tell what we have?" I asked.

"It looks like somebody has poured a lot of red dirt (East Tennessee red clay) along with some loose rocks, sticks and a few pop bottles into this entire corner."

"How can you tell the entire corner is bad?"

"Well I can't for sure but the further down this line I go, the more loose red dirt keeps falling back into the ditch."

We knew we had to keep digging until we hit undisturbed ground. Building on loose fill would guarantee the footer would fail and the entire right rear corner of the house would settle. At around 9 feet we finally hit undisturbed red clay.

"Well, I better call Mr. Harrington," I said. "We can't do anything else until we can resolve this issue and we can't spend this kind of money without his approval. Billy is there anything else you can do until I can get this resolved."

"Not really, I can't do much else until I get the footers dug. I could start hauling rock but it will just end up being in the way," Billy said.

"Ok Billy, I'll call you tonight and let you know what's next."

"Well Chub, I'll have to be able to work here tomorrow. If not, I will have to move over to that job in Greene County. I can't let this equipment sit here idle for an entire day and once I move it I can't come back for about a week."

"I understand," I said. "Mr. Harrington is a smart guy and I think he will understand what has to be done. I'll call you tonight."

The entire corner comprising 53 linear feet and anywhere from 3' to 12' on either side of the footing line was bad. Mr. Harrington left work and was on site within an hour of my call.

"Chub, I hope you're not going to hit me with a lot more money at this stage." Mr. Harrington stated as he exited his car.

"I'm not hitting you with anything," I said feeling a little pissed. "This is what we've run into and the simple fact is the developer has apparently filled the entire back half of this lot with loose red dirt in order to flatten out the lot. We have about 143 cubic yards of fill that is going to have to removed and then filled back with number 57 stone. That's just to take care of the footer and the basement floor area."

"What is that going to cost?" Harrington asked.

"We're not sure yet but the gravel alone would require 143 cubic yards x 2,600 lbs. per yard. That would be 186 tons of gravel at $27 per ton plus the haul bill. That's $5,022 plus $60 a load for hauling. Each truck holds about 22 tons so that's 9 loads x $60 will be another $540 for hauling. Billy's already spent a couple of extra hours and it will take him about a day to dig out the 143 yards."

"All day at $75 an hour?" Harrington exclaimed!!

"Yes sir, if he can do it that quick. That's as much or more cubic yards as came out of the basement," I said.

"That's as much as the entire excavation was supposed to cost. How could you miss your estimate that bad?" Harrington complained.

"Whoa buddy, I didn't miss anything. The original estimate still stands as I quoted you. There is no way we could predict this."

"Well I know this," Harrington started, "I can't afford another $6,000 or $7,000 for just excavation".

"Believe me I understand that. Here is what I suggest, you need to go to the developer and tell him that he needs to either trade this lot for another or he needs to pay for these extras. If he prefers he can bring in his own equipment and fix it himself."

"My wife and I love this lot."

"That's fine" I said, "but you need to either work this out with the developer or be willing to pay for these extras."

"I don't want to get started off on the wrong foot in this neighborhood," Harrington argued. "Besides he'll just say it's not his fault."

"He can say whatever he wants," I said, "but this lot is full of loose fill. If it's not his fault whose is it then?"

"Well I'm not too sure it's not yours" Harrington said.

I'm sure my face was as red as a diaper rash on a baby's butt when I replied, "Look Dumbass, you know it's not my fault and if you think the developer's tough to deal with just keep up with this crap! The simple fact is you were sold a lot that has been filled. We can't build your house on it and probably can't run the septic lines if we don't fix this issue. The developer is responsible. I've told you what you need to do. You need to either make this guy fix this or sign a change order for me. There is a clause in the contract covering this issue. I personally explained it to you before you signed it. If Billy doesn't work here tomorrow he won't be back here for at least a week. I'm going home now. When you make up your mind, call me and I will act accordingly."

As you can see this situation was difficult. The homeowner was not willing to face a potentially unpleasant situation, even for $7,000, and was determined to act as if his was the only building lot in the world. The moral to this story is twofold. First, talk to the neighbors and the developer to hopefully learn as much as possible about the original condition of the lot. The developer is obligated to tell you if he has filled any part of the lot. Asking a neighbor can often lead to finding out valuable information that may not be readily available. Second, don't fall so much in love with a lot that you're willing to be stupid over it. The homeowner in this story decided to pay for the extras himself and continued to resent me because of it. As the project proceeded we had to remove even more loose-fill to install the septic system and to support the large deck. Of course he blamed that on me too. What should have been a pleasant experience turned out to be a very long five months for everyone involved.

It's Such a Great Deal

I took a deep breath and said, "If it were me I would not buy this lot." The Adams looked at each other like they had just lost their jobs.

"Really, but why?" Mrs. Adams asked.

"Well, if you look around there are numerous places where rock is showing."

"What exactly do you mean by showing?"

"By showing, I mean there are large rocks sticking up out of the ground in many places."

"This is a really big lot," she replied, "and there are a lot more places that don't have rock showing than there are that do."

"This lot is two and a half acres," her husband added, "and besides, this is such a great deal on this piece of property."

"That's all true," I said, "but you have to wonder, if it's such a great deal why hasn't one of the builders in the subdivision scooped it up before now?"

I could see that my concerns were falling on deaf ears. Being the glutton for punishment that I am, I decided to keep expressing my opinion. "It's true that these rock formations are spread out and there are a lot of places where rock is not showing, but to me that is actually more problematic. Rock showing in multiple locations can often mean the presence of a large connected rock formation."

"Are you a geologist?" she asked me as if talking to a fourth grader.

"No Ma'am, I am not. But you might want to consider hiring one or a soil scientist before you commit to buying this property."

"How much would that cost?" the husband asked.

"I'm not sure, but I would guess a couple of thousand dollars at least."

"Maybe we could get the developer to pay that or agree to remove the rock," she said.

"Well I don't see that happening but I guess you could try," I said.

"If he wants to sell the lot he will."

Yeah right, I thought to myself, trying not to laugh. Speaking to her husband Mrs. Adams said, "Jerry, I want this lot. I love the view, the privacy, and you love the fact there is so much land."

"Yes dear, I suppose I could talk to the developer on Monday."

"Well Mr. Chubby Builder, what do you have to say about that?" she said with a smirk.

"Yes Ma'am, that's fine with me. I do have one suggestion. We should consider looking at going back into the trees and see if there might be a suitable building spot back in there. Often on a piece of property like this, trees grow where a rock formation ends."

"Absolutely not", she said, "we will not be removing any trees on this lot."

"All righty then," I said, "Just let me know what you decide."

Towards the end of the following week I got a call from Mr. Adams. "Mr. Chubby Builder, I talked to the developer and he refused to do anything about the rock. According to him, the lot is two and one half acres meaning there should be plenty of places to build a 2,500 square foot house."

"Yes sir," I said, "but more than an acre of that are trees and your wife said there would be no trees cut at all."

"Well Mr. Chubby Builder to be honest, the developer said you really didn't know what you were talking about on the rock. He said that rock spread around didn't mean anything."

"Well sir, that's probably true. I'm quite sure that a developer would never stretch the truth just to sell a lot," I replied sarcastically.

"Nonetheless, we have decided that we are going ahead with the project and we don't want to waste money hiring a soil scientist. Now do you still want to build this house or should we hire someone else?"

"Yes sir, I still want to build it, but please be aware there is a rock clause in my or any other builder's contract saying we would not be responsible for whatever sub-surface conditions we might find."

"Yes, yes, I know about rock clauses, when can you start?"

On the second day of excavation and within about 5 feet of finishing the basement excavation, the loader operator heard the screech of his metal bucket hitting rock. The large vein was about six feet long and four feet wide, and it jutted out from the front left corner of the basement. After weighing all of the options, the homeowner decided the best option was to move the house back six feet. I preferred to blast and remove the rock from the corner, because by moving the house back we would be unable to share a poured concrete wall section between the basement and the garage. That meant there would a gap between the wall and the garage slab that had to be filled with stone or even worse concrete

Of course I was over ruled again, and the surveyor was called back in to reset the corners at a cost of $500. The next day as we excavated the back portion of the basement and within about 18 inches of grade we hit another vein of rock. This time, after consulting with the poured wall contractor, we convinced the homeowner the best course of action was to chip out eight inches of rock inside the basement area and 18 inches where the footing crossed the rock vein. We then raised the grade of the basement floor with 12 inches of compacted gravel and went from 9 foot basement walls to 10 foot basement walls. The total cost of all these measures was about $12,000 to which the homeowner replied, "I knew this would happen. It's ridiculous that you people charge so much for something like moving some rock."

In the end we were required to remove rock for the septic system, the garage, and the rear deck. The driveway had to be extended about 150 feet more than should have been necessary and several of the trees had to be removed. In all, there was more than $40,000 in costs directly related to problems caused by rock. But hey, they got a killer deal on that lot!

Other Location Considerations

Orientation

Because the sun rises in the east and sets in the west, at the equator the sun moves across the southern sky in the northern hemisphere and the northern sky in the southern hemisphere. Therefore it is very important to consider orientation of your home when choosing a place to build your dream home. Too often homes are built without considering how interior atmosphere and utility cost will be affected by the position of the sun. The proper orientation for your new home depends on personal preference and the climate you live in. For example, in the northern half of the United States where heating is more of a priority than cooling, there are many advantages to having the wall with the most glass facing south. Heat from the sun will help warm those areas of your house in the winter and take advantage of natural lighting year round. Even in the coldest climates it's not unusual to see many houses built with a garage on the southern end of a house, thus taking no advantage of the natural heating and lighting benefits of the sun. Likewise in the Deep South, with mild winters and long brutal summers, it may be better to have most of the glass on the house facing north, east or west. Regardless of where you build, orientation is a vital consideration in the overall comfort and indoor atmosphere of your new home. Any efforts here will be rewarded with lower utility bills in the future.

Price and Affordability

The general rule says that a lots price should be no more than about 25% of the cost of the house. So if you're planning on spending a total of $100,000 then you should not pay more than $25,000 for your lot. If spending $200,000, then you should not pay more than $50,000 for the lot and so on. Likewise, most experts agree that the cost of housing (meaning mortgage, taxes, and utilities) should not exceed 25 to 30% of a family's monthly income. That's a pretty good rule for you, and it's good to remember when considering the future value of your home when it's time to sell.

Chapter Two

Design Considerations and Value Engineering

> ***"Perfection is achieved, not when there is nothing more to add, but when there is nothing left to take away."–Antoine de Saint – Exupery, Airman's Odyssey***

The above quote really referred to airplanes but it's also relevant to home design. Home design is best when it strives to adhere to the principles of the "Golden Mean" defined by the Greek philosopher Aristotle as, "The desirable middle between two extremes, one of excess and one of deficiency."

The best way to achieve the "Golden Mean", and more importantly make yourself and your family happiest in the long run, is to first decide what is really important. If your funds are unlimited none of this probably matters. For the vast majority of us, we have to compromise and adjust to make our projects work. The first thing I talk about at every initial meeting with a potential client is the importance of a family meeting. The meeting is to determine what is most important for each family member and then weed out anything that is not imperative. At that point, what's left is negotiated until there's a consensus.

Make all necessary changes before applying for permits. The design and planning stage is the time to make the important decisions. If a client wants to be happy with the finished product and bring the project in on budget, it's imperative that all the decisions are made before construction begins.

The design of a custom home is controlled primarily by the homeowner's personal tastes and desires. However optimal design requires consideration of certain fundamentals. First, a basic understanding of landscape design is helpful to decide where to place the home on the property and to choose the overall exterior appearance. A general rule is the distance from street to the house should be at least the width of the house because the optimal horizontal angle for viewing a near object is 45 degrees. On a large lot with a hilltop, the home should be placed slightly below the top of the hill in order to create balance.

Most zoning authorities require minimum setbacks from each property line. For example in our jurisdiction the setback from the front property line is 30 feet. The side property-lines are 15 feet and the rear setback is 25 feet. A typical half acre lot in our area will have a width of 100 feet making the maximum width of the building 70 feet. It is also common for utilities like electric, water and telephone to have their own setback. In our area that setback is 15 feet from the face of the curb to the property line, so no part of the building can be closer to the street than 45 feet. When I say no part of the building, it's important to note that these setbacks include roof overhangs, porches gables etc. The setbacks are enforced vertically. To illustrate, enforced vertically means if a home in our area was built with the roof overhang ending at exactly 45 feet from the face of the curb and you added 6 inch guttering that would be a violation, because the house would only be setback 44 feet six inches. That may seem trivial but if there was ever a property line dispute or any reason for it to be checked (like at inspection time), it could be a serious problem.

Every year seemingly minor violations end up in court in most jurisdictions in the country. I always make sure I leave myself a foot of extra space on each property line to be safe. I also never build a house without hiring a surveyor to mark the property lines and the house corners. Many builders will tell you surveyors are a waste of money and they have "laid out hundreds of houses". I promise the penalties for mistakes can be severe. This brings me to the next real life example.

That Can't Be Right; We Must Have Measured It Ten Times!

A longtime friend of mine is an experienced homebuilder that does quality work and has an excellent reputation. In 2009 he was approached by a client for whom he had built three homes, two for himself and one for his daughter. Having hired my friend three times and inquiring about a fourth it is safe to assume he was pleased with Roger's work. Don't hold me to the exact numbers, but Roger had given the client a very detailed estimate of about $350,000. Within a week the client returned to Roger and told him he had a quote from another builder for $265,000. My friend explained to the gentleman there was no way the guy could build this house for that price. Look Roger said, "I didn't just make these numbers up. You have a detailed estimate showing you exactly how each dollar would be spent and you have always been happy with our work." To make a long story short, the client said there was just too much price difference. He had to go with the competing $265,000 bid. These are just a few things that happened in this story:

- When the first round of suppliers invoices came due, the builder could not pay all of the invoices. The owner had to pay the balance and personally guarantee the accounts or the material deliveries would be cut off.
- Subcontractors started walking off the job because of either non-payment or slow payment.
- For some inexplicable reason, the builder had installed the hardwood floor before the sheetrock (wall board) was installed and painted. He covered it up as if he expected rosin paper to protect it. This made it necessary to completely strip and refinish the entire floor.
- By the third draw, the bank refused any more funding.
- Since there were no detailed specifications the builder had installed the HVAC system, the plumbing fixtures, and the kitchen appliances with the absolute cheapest products he could find, even buying a refurbished dishwasher. He installed all of this much too early in an apparent attempt to force the homeowner into accepting the sub-standard products.

- The builder's workman's compensation insurance had expired making it necessary for the homeowner to pay for an emergency room visit or face a potential lawsuit.
- And my favorite, which is why I included this story in this chapter, the entire 75 foot x 4 foot retaining wall and part of the driveway were built on someone else's property. Of course the builder had laid this out himself because "a surveyor was a big waste of money" and "that couldn't possibly be right, we must have measured it ten times".

The homeowner and the builder fought constantly. The house had not been completed after more than two years. The bank had to hire another contactor to finish the home and foreclose after the homeowner and his wife got a divorce and no longer paid the payments. The last I heard everybody was suing everybody. As far as I know it still hasn't been settled. The reason I know so much detail is because I live in the neighborhood. Unbelievably the homeowner had constantly called my friend to complain about the other builder and to ask for free advice. There are many lessons in this story, but proper planning and due diligence reside at the top. That is also why you always hire a surveyor.

Have It Your Way

Buying a suitable plan or having the right plan designed for you is not only doable, it's the easy part. After you have decided what features will make everyone in the family happy, you then need to set a budget. While it may seem better to set the budget first, I have found working out the features first is the best way to insure getting the "most bang for your buck". By first vetting out the features most important to everyone at the start, all the issues come out early. Everyone's opinion is considered without letting the budget get in the way of creativity. With this approach it is much easier to go back and make the cuts necessary to stay within the budget because everyone's opinion and desires have been considered. Most family members can understand that money is not unlimited. They often care more about having their desires considered than they do actually getting what they want. It sets the process up to simplify the elimination of items, which will bring less value than they cost.

When setting a budget it's important to be realistic about what the family can actually afford. Keep in mind that financial institutions are pretty adamant. Total cost of housing including mortgage payment, utilities, taxes, insurance and maintenance is no more than 25% to 30% of a household's monthly income. These standard ratios are based on the industry's years of experience with millions of homeowners. So it only makes sense to consider them when building your budget. Don't forget that you need to make a list of specifications as you go. For example, if you want Delta faucets and Kitchen Aid appliances you need to list that before seeking an estimate, so you will have a detailed specification sheet in your contract with the contractor.

Standard Design Considerations

A custom home design is all about your unique desires and requirements; however many things tend to appear again and again in elegant design. In this case, elegant means efficient, affordable and appealing.

Curb Appeal

The front view of your house should entice anyone viewing from the street to imagine what the home looks like inside. Does it inspire a warm and welcoming feeling? If a buyer were to see your home after seeing dozens of others, would yours stand out while still being tasteful? Do the materials and colors used balance with the surrounding landscape? Is the look unique yet still comparable to the other homes in the neighborhood or general area?

The same house in a rural setting will often appear much different than it would in a suburban setting. As I mentioned before, where a home is placed on a property can really affect the view from the street.

Factors in Curb Appeal

The front elevation is the first thing people notice from the street. It should be where ninety percent of the money for exterior appearance is spent. The most important factors for curb appeal are the lines and angles comprising the ground line, the gables, the overhangs, the roof ridge line, the choice of exterior cladding or siding, roof pitches, doors and windows, roofing materials, porches, and of course landscaping.

Lines and Angles

The best way to enhance ground lines is to offset walls. I have found that having a front elevation with 3 slightly different horizontal ground lines is a great way to dress up the front of the house. Too many different lines will increase costs without adding any real value to the look. In some cases having more than 3 different horizontal ground lines can create a confusing and messy look. Also keep in mind more corners means higher costs. Often a house with a width of less than fifty feet looks great with just two horizontal ground offsets, which will definitely save some money. A good example is a continuous horizontal line on the main part of the house and a 3-5 foot offset on the garage with the garage gable facing the street.

Roof angles like higher pitches and changing pitches add character. Be careful with roof pitches though, because this can backfire if overdone. If for example the house sits slightly below the level of the street, it will look best if the roof pitch isn't too steep. After all, you don't want the view of your home to be all roof. Likewise, if the home sits above the road a steeper pitch is better. High roof pitches like 10/12 and 12/12 can add significantly to building costs which I'll discuss in greater depth when we get to value engineering.

Cladding and Siding

The exterior walls of the home will look much better with some variety. For the most part I recommend using no more than two different materials (brick and stone or brick and lap siding for example). I've seen houses with three different wall materials look pretty good, but anything more is way too busy.

This is just my opinion, but if there is any way you can afford a brick home you should use it. No other cladding material has more built in benefits than brick. I have seen a few homes where I didn't necessarily agree with a choice of brick style, yet I can honestly say I have never seen a brick home I thought was ugly. Brick insulates better than any other siding material, takes pretty much zero maintenance, lasts for centuries and always looks great. If a hurricane or a tornado is flinging debris at one hundred mph, there's no place I would rather be than in a brick home. My favorite look is brick with a few stone accents.

Now not everyone can afford a house built with all brick and stone, and some people prefer the look of siding. I have used just about everything made to clad exterior walls. Without a doubt the best horizontal lap siding and the best vertical siding (board and batten) I've seen are the fiber cement products from the "James Hardie Corporation". I have used these products for every single home I have built since the product came out. I sometimes used it for the entire house, yet have always used it as either an accent or as trim around the eves and in gables. It is now available in factory painted colors where it is the same color all the way through the material. The painted version has a 20 year warranty against fading. They even offer it in cedar shake style. Before you think this is a commercial for Hardie planks, I assure you the company has no idea I even exist. I just love the product. I have projects including some commercial buildings, built more than 10 years ago and every one of them look as good today as the day the material was installed. The only disadvantage is whoever cuts it must use a face mask because breathing in the fibers is not a good idea. I doubt breathing in wood saw dust would do you much good either.

As a last resort, and if you must, you can use vinyl siding. It's the least expensive alternative; however it takes much more maintenance than any of the other choices. Supposedly you do not need to paint it, but in my experience darker colors fade faster than painted wood. The only houses we built that I'm not proud were houses where we used too much vinyl.

Roofs

Roof lines can have a huge effect on the looks of a home but can also be a source of budget busting waste. Most builders tend to start their careers building homes with very low pitched roofs like 3/12, 4/12 or 5/12. I, on the other hand, went in the opposite direction with my first few homes having roof pitches of 12/12. To illustrate what these ratios mean, a roof with a 4/12 pitch means that for every 12" a roof runs horizontally it will drop or slope 4" inches vertically. So if you have a 6/12 roof, the roof pitch is half the width. To further illustrate, if the top ridge of a roof section is say 50 feet long from side to side and the slope is 6/12, then the ridgeline down to the eave would be 25 feet.

Placed on a level lot the higher the pitch, the more roofing will be visible. As mentioned earlier, as a general rule if the house sits below the street level you want less roof slope and if it sits above the street more is better. Never use a roof pitch under 6/12 because in my opinion a 4/12 roof looks like a mobile home. In fact, most mobile homes have a roof pitch of either 3/12 or 4/12.

Architects love to design homes with steep roof pitches, especially if someone else is paying for it like with a custom job. The first few houses we built I bought the plans from a popular local architect who loved huge roofs with 12/12 pitches, very cut up with the roof having multiple angles and directions. After the third project we realized we were wasting a ton of money. The roofs were so large and complex we couldn't make manufactured trusses work. Everything had to be stick framed (one board at a time, cut to size with complicated mitered cuts at the top and bottom) which created a lot of extra work and expense. We spent $40,000 to $50,000 on some of the roofs alone. Roof framing that would have taken a few days using trusses were taking 4 and 5 weeks to stick frame costing 3 or 4 times as much in labor, which by the way is the single highest cost in most building projects.

Many inexperienced builders make the same mistake we did because purchasing engineered trusses is higher than purchasing a roofing package consisting of 2x6's or 2x8's. What it takes a few projects to realize is labor costs and lost time will far exceed the extra material cost associated with using engineered trusses. In addition, I like something that is engineered versus built in the field by carpenters who may or may not have a grasp of load factors.

When designing our current home my wife and I modified an existing plan that originally had a 12/12 roof design and converted it to an 8/12. If I had it to do over, I would have gone 6/12. Over the last 10 years or so we have made a concentrated effort to build using only 6/12 pitched roofs whenever possible. The 6/12 roofs are the perfect balance between curb appeal and cost.

There about as many roof covering materials as there are roof types. Traditional asphalt shingles come in two main types. Standard asphalt shingles called 3 tabs are the least expensive. Depending on who you talk to, they can be the easiest to install. I personally don't like 3 tab shingles because they look cheap and they do not last very long. They tend to mold and the absolute highest rating they are available in is 20 or 25 year. My favorite shingle is the asphalt shingle referred to as architectural or dimensional shingles. They have a very balanced and pleasing look and come with warranties between 30 to 50 years. Most reputable brands come with anti-mold agents that keep them looking good for a long time. Dimensional shingles are about 20% more expensive than the least expensive 3 tabs but are worth every penny. Every home I've built for the last 10 years has been built with either dimensional shingles or metal roofing.

Another popular choice for roofing material is the metal roof. Metal roofing had always been considerably more expensive than asphalt roofing until about 2004 or so when oil prices started to rise. While still a little more expensive, the closing price gap made metal roofing a much more viable option in recent years. As of this writing the trend in long term oil prices is predicted to be much lower, so if you're considering a metal roof you may want to take the leap sooner rather than later. Metal roofs come in a variety of colors and most carry warranties of 50 years or more.

Other types of roofing materials include natural slate, traditional clay tile, wood shakes and a few different modern composite coverings. Slate and clay tiles can last as much as 100 years but because of both material costs and the extra weight, they are both considerably more expensive. Either requires a significant "beefing up" of framing, increasing framing costs by 30-40%. The one time I actually considered installing a tile roof, on a home of about 2,400 square feet, the total cost increase from dimensional shingles to barrel clay tile rose from around $17,000 to over $50,000. I don't have enough experience or knowledge with wood shakes or the new composites to provide you with much information. I know wood is pretty expensive and will increase flammability but I cannot comment beyond that. I have heard some good things about some of the composites, but with both wood and composites I just recommend that you do a lot of research and due diligence before considering them.

Overhangs, Gables and Porches

Over the years I've built homes with roof overhangs from 12 inches to over 2 feet. In my opinion, unless the architect can give you a very good reason, anything over 18 inches is a waste and anything over 12 inches is unnecessary. It may not seem important until you get the price for material and labor necessary to run hundreds of feet of soffit. This is one place I really recommend vinyl. It works great with little maintenance and saves money.

Having a front facing gable can add a lot of character to the look of a house, usually over a garage, porch or offset. With a front facing gable I recommend you increase the roof pitch of the gable by a couple of inches. In other words, if your main roof is 6/12 then make the gable's slope 8/12 or 10/12. The gable is also a great place for a third cladding material. Let's say all the exterior walls are covered with either brick or stone. The gable will look great with either a cedar shake pattern or a lapped plank siding made of either Hardie Plank or heavy gauge vinyl.

Front porches or stoops are not only functional but done correctly can add both value and tons of curb appeal. Columns do more to add class to a porch than any other feature. I absolutely love 10 inch round columns. I put 8 inch round columns on my house and 10 inch on a house built in the same neighborhood. Let me tell you there is all the difference in the world. The 10 inch columns make my neighbors medium size house look like a mansion from the street. The difference is unbelievable. A feature making a comeback is a round column set atop a square box about 12 to 24 inches high and built out of brick or framed with 2x4's and covered with Hardie Board or siding. Porches also benefit from railings. I've had the best luck with vinyl clad railing featuring square balusters 3 to 4 inches apart, specifically made for round columns. Most building codes will require railings on any porch with a finished floor level from 12" to 30" or more above finished grade.

Windows

Windows work in conjunction with orientation to bring natural light and heat into a home. The placement of windows has as much influence on the inside atmosphere as on the outside. As I write this I am sitting at my kitchen table on a beautiful October morning next to three south facing windows. The windows sit in a small bay area with the two 32" windows placed at a 45 degree angle and joined together by a 36" window running parallel to the main wall. The blinds on the angled windows are open and the blinds on the 36" window facing directly south are closed. The main living area has a set of full glass French doors facing due south with egress to a covered deck and there is a 72" mulled double window about 6 feet east of the French door. This entire area is bright and pleasing. Although the temperatures dipped into the high thirties this morning we have not needed any heat because the light from the sun has provided just the right amount of heat to make the rooms very comfortable. I don't have a single light on and with the one blind closed the light needed for writing is perfect.

The master bedroom is on the west end of the main floor with a second master suite on the east end. All of the areas where we live are on the south end of the house with the walk in closets, formal dining room, garage and a small formal living room on the north side. The bathrooms sit between the closets and the bedrooms, with a single glass block window in each bath, facing west in the main master and east is the second master suite. I describe my home in detail to illustrate the benefits of proper orientation and window placement. Of the fourteen windows in my home, eight are on the south side of the house. The natural light provided is by far our favorite feature and the standout feature for anyone who visits.

Window Types and Materials

There are about eleven basic types of windows readily available for residential construction today. Below is a short description of each with the advantages and disadvantages of different materials available.

- **Fixed** – This type of window has a fixed or non-opening pane of glass. It is used mainly to bring in light over front doors or other windows to brighten foyers etc.

- **Single Hung**– I use single hung windows more than any other type. They have a top and bottom sash but only the bottom operates. Using these windows is a great way to save money, especially if used on the ground floor where cleaning the top sash from the outside is no big deal. The bottom sashes on most modern single hung windows also tilt in for easier cleaning. Heck, if you're like me, you clean your windows once every 3-5 years whether they need it or not.

- **Double hung** – I often recommend my clients install these in upper story bedrooms because both sashes operate and both tilt in for easier cleaning. Both sashes move up and down sliding past each other. Most only allow you to open one sash at a time.

- **Casement –** Another of my favorites, casement windows are hinged on the side, much like a door and are operated using a hand crank. I usually recommend going with the top quality casements because a cheap opening mechanism will cause you problems down the road.

- **Awning** – Awning windows are similar to casement windows but are hinged at the top or bottom. They can also have two sections, one hinged at the top and one at the bottom.

- **Jalousie** – Rarely used in modern home construction, Jalousie windows are multiple narrow panes of glass that open together with a single crank.

- **Sliding** – Sliding windows move side to side on tracks similar to a sliding glass door. These tend to be inexpensive.

- **Palladian**– A Palladian window consists of a group of three windows mulled together with an arched window above, usually just over the middle window.

- **Picture** – These are large fixed windows with operating widows on either side.

- **Clerestory** – Clerestory windows are a series of small panes mulled together. The panes are almost always fixed and are usually used above doors or other windows.

- **Elliptical or Arched** – Elliptical or arched windows are often placed above doors and other windows, mainly for aesthetics and to bring in extra light to rooms on the north end of the home.

Window Materials

- **Aluminum –** Aluminum windows are fairly inexpensive. The home I grew up in had aluminum windows and I wouldn't put them in a dog house.

- **Vinyl – In** the part of East Tennessee where I operate, vinyl windows are very popular. They are my favorite because they come in nearly every style and size, open and close easily, are maintenance free, and are very reasonably priced. Like anything else, you do not want to go with a low end vinyl window. You get what you pay for here. I've had good luck with Silverline, Weathershield, and Simonton. Sunrise and Marvin windows have a very good reputation, but I don't have any experience with them.

- **Wood –** Wood windows are beautiful, but expensive. They must be painted and maintained, and they tend to expand and contract with temperature variations. Over the long run moisture and rotting can become a problem. I highly recommend both Anderson and Pella wood windows. Neither brand is cheap, but the quality and performance are outstanding.

- **Vinyl Clad Wood –** These windows are the best of both worlds. The insides are made of wood and come in both natural and painted finishes. You can order them pre-primed or order them unfinished and paint or stain them. The outside is wood covered with vinyl, making them maintenance free and protecting them from moisture. These products are both beautiful and expensive. Again you can't go wrong with Anderson or Pella.

- **Fiberglass and Composite –** Fiberglass and composite windows have less than 3% of the market share in the residential window market, mainly due to cost. They are an excellent choice if you have the budget for them. They are price competitive with some vinyl clad wood windows, but typically run 30 to 60% higher than vinyl. The biggest advantage to fiberglass/composite windows is they expand and contract at the same rate as the glass inside, making them maintenance free for many years. They can be painted or stained. They are sold pre-painted too. I do not have enough experience with these windows to make a brand recommendation, but "Consumer Reports" and others do cover and rate them.

- **Exterior Doors –** I do not want to write much about exterior doors because I have only one recommendation - fiberglass. For years we always purchased metal doors because they were less expensive. We never built a house where we weren't forced to replace at least one door. Metal doors get dinged so easily it's nearly impossible to get through an entire project without screwing one up. Since we started using fiberglass we have never had to replace a door; net/net they're less expensive. They can be painted or stained and come in both wood grain and smooth. I have always used the Masonite brand fiberglass door and have always been satisfied.

Balancing Window Placement for Exterior Appearance and Interior Function

There are some basics for window placement that will enhance the look of a home. None are hard and fast rules but useful guidelines.

- Whenever possible stack windows in a multi-story house over each other for balance.
- Keep window sizes to three or less. This is not a hard and fast rule, yet it does work well.

- Use windows that are taller than they are wide. I nearly always use windows that are five feet tall and either 32 or 36 inches wide.
- In most rooms, center the window on the outside wall. For example, if the exterior wall of the room is 12 feet the center of the window would be at 6 feet.

The exception to the last rule is in bedrooms. From the first house I built to the last I will ever build, bedroom windows go in the corners. This spreads the light more evenly. More importantly, it significantly increases the options for furniture placement, thus making the room more livable.

Efficiency ratings for Windows:

You'll see these numbers on Energy Star and National Fenestration Rating Council (NFRC) window labels.

U-factor, or U-value, usually ranges from 0.20 to 1.20. The lower the number the better the window is at keeping heat in.

Solar heat gain coefficient (SHGC) is between 0 and 1. The lower the number the better the window is at blocking unwanted heat from the sun. In warm climates you'll want the lowest number you can find; in cold areas a higher number is better.

Visible transmittance (VT) indicates how much visible light a window lets in and is between 0 and 1. As the number increases so does the light.

Value Engineering

Wikipedia defines value engineering like this:

Value engineering (**VE**) is a systematic method to improve the "value" of goods or products and services by using an examination of function. Value, as defined, is the ratio of function to cost. Value can therefore be increased by either improving the function or reducing the cost. It is a primary tenet of value engineering that basic functions be preserved and not be reduced as a consequence of pursuing value improvements.

In our use of value engineering for housing, we never make a change unless it improves the functionality, the quality, or reduces cost. Cost is the last consideration for us because we don't want to sacrifice anything that reduces "livability" just to save a little money. In most cases we are talking only a little money because value engineering, done properly, is an investment that reduces cost in the long run.

Foundations

For many, many years in East Tennessee, nearly all foundations were built with hollow concrete block. Now don't get me wrong, with a crawl space of 4 feet tall or less and having no backfill against it, concrete block is sufficient. In my opinion, concrete block should not be used for a basement and should never be used if backfill (soil) is placed against it. Under no circumstances should a block wall taller than four feet be built without filling it with concrete, steel rebar, and waterproofing. Most codes would not allow it anyway; however some places don't have building inspections. I'll cover more about codes later, but the point here is many people will cut corners on the foundation. Every part of a home rests on the quality of the foundation.

The foundation fails and everything fails. I can't tell you how many homes in this part of the country have foundation walls that are buckling, leaking or settling. There is an entire multi-billion dollar industry devoted to nothing but repairing failing foundations. Believe me it is not cheap to fix a failing foundation.

There are more options for foundation and basement walls available today than ever before. Below are some examples with pros and cons of each.

Concrete Block – I talked about this; I'm not a fan. Acceptable if filled with concrete and steel rebar to code, but still difficult to waterproof. I have used these for small crawl spaces and to build boundaries for a concrete slab. Blocks are fine for crawl spaces less than 4 feet tall.

Insulated Concrete Forms (ICF) – These are Styrofoam blocks that are similar in size to a 12" concrete block. These are filled with concrete and tied to the footings with rebar. The best feature of ICF construction is the high R-value (insulation value). Depending on the brand and construction of the ICF, R-values can run between R-30 to as much as R-50. To compare, a typical un-insulated 8 inch poured concrete wall is approximately R-1.35.

ICF's have design flexibility similar to concrete block, are easier to waterproof than block, and are termite resistant. This is an excellent choice as the quality is high, they are sturdy and with such high R-values they will eventually pay for themselves. The only drawback is the high upfront expense. ICF construction is one of the most expensive methods of building a basement. In addition, they do not work well for an unfinished basement because the foam block is exposed.

Poured Concrete Walls – When all things are considered poured walls are my favorite. At first glance they are more expensive than block, but don't be fooled. If concrete block is filled with mortar and rebar it is as expensive, if not more so, than poured walls. Many people make the mistake of not taking all these costs into consideration. Never use hollow concrete block higher than 3-4 feet without reinforcement with mortar and rebar.

Poured walls are built using large aluminum forms, where a rebar cage is built both horizontally and vertically inside the form. The form is then filled with high strength concrete. After 24-48 hours the aluminum forms are removed leaving a solid continuous wall. Poured walls are placed at 6, 8, 10 or 12 inches thick depending on the loads created by backfill. Because they are solid and continuous, poured walls are the easiest to waterproof allowing for waterproofing warranties up to lifetime. Overall, poured walls are designed and built faster than any other method. A large basement can usually be set, poured and stripped in a total of three days with an additional day to waterproof. The only negative is that it is important you find a poured wall subcontractor who really knows what they are doing and stand behind their work. I have used two different poured wall subs in my career. The first company got the job done but seemed to have something wrong on every job mainly for failing to follow up on all the details. My present poured wall sub-contractor is great. They have the crew, the expertise, and the proper equipment. Every job has been perfect.

Superior Walls® – We've built a total of 16 homes using Superior Walls® including my own personal home I built twelve years ago. As a builder, I absolutely love them. I have never had the first complaint. The basements are bone dry without any waterproofing because the panels are made of 5,000 psi concrete, which is so dense water will not penetrate it. If your builder is organized and prepared there is nothing faster. Once the walls are on site, they are set and ready for subfloor in a day or less. The builder needs to be organized because he needs the site to be prepared while the walls are designed and built, which usually takes a week or so. The corners need to be set, excavation complete and six inches of compacted (1/2" max) stone needs to be in place.

I quit using Superior Walls® several years ago and switched to poured walls, only because the contractor that installed them for us had a falling out with Superior Walls® Corporate. The people that installed our walls were very smart and super professional. I just was not sure that a less experienced sub-contractor could do the job. It is very important with this product to use someone with a good reputation and a lot of experience setting them. In researching this book I searched the internet to see if the company had any complaints. There were only about three and they all seemed to be about the same contractor. The product is great; however like anything else, it must be properly installed.

There are of course other products and methods available. Yet these are the ones I have the most experience with and would recommend.

Framing Options

We have used many different types of framing systems including engineered metal packages, metal studs, structural insulated panels (SIPS), traditional wood framing, and advanced wood framing (also referred to as OVE or optimal value engineering). Each of these methods has advantages and disadvantages. Each option should be considered according to your objectives and budget.

Engineered Metal Packages and Metal Studs

If money was not a consideration I would build this way every time. As late as the mid-1990s very few homes in the U.S. were built with metal framing, although it's been widely used in Japan since the 1940s. Today about 20% of American homes are built using steel framing.

While the cost of a steel stud is usually comparable in price to a wood 2x4 stud, the overall cost of framing with metal will be about 15-20% higher. The main reason is a metal framing system must be engineered as well as designed. This could be partially offset by picking a design that is a stock plan sold by the metal supplier. Of course that may defeat your purpose of building a custom home. Besides the price of framing, the thermal properties of metal (tendency to attract heat and cold) can increase the cost of heating and cooling a home by as much as 15%. The good news is most of this cost can be offset by using Styrofoam insulation panels in addition to wood sheathing.

Certainly upfront cost and energy efficiency are important considerations. However these two considerations can be significantly offset with savings elsewhere and by every other measure metal is superior.

Metal framing is stronger making it much more resistant to disasters like hurricanes, tornadoes and earthquakes. Metal framing is also fire resistant. Because there are no chemical additives, air quality is better. Most insurance companies offer a significant discount for metal framing. Metal is water and insect resistant and environmentally friendlier as there is no waste to transport to landfills or burn. The metal is also 100% recyclable. As a builder I really like that all the holes are already there for utilities and everything is precut, so no waste and no sawdust. Just assemble each piece according to the blueprint. The most impressive thing about metal framing is the quality. Every wall, every floor, every ceiling, and every roof is perfectly straight and square. Using metal also allows longer spans, providing the ability to design larger open areas without a need for load bearing interior walls.

Structural Insulated Panels (SIPS)

We really liked using structural insulated wall panels. We used these a few times when we did our own framing and they are quick and easy to use. SIPS are pre-built walls that are basically 6-8 inches of foam insulation sandwiched between OSB or plywood. They come up to 10 feet tall and the length of each section is determined according to the plan. Each section is numbered, and like the metal framing, you just put the panel where the blueprint says.

These things allow for R-values up to about R-30 in walls and R-48 in roof panels. They already have all the holes cut and pipes run for electric, phone cable, and plumbing. Because they are pre-insulated, you skip an entire construction phase. The big drawback is they are expensive. Considering only material costs, SIPS are about 55-60%

higher than conventional framing. For the builder, labor costs of installing SIPS are about one-half that of conventional framing. However unless you can find framers with SIP experience it can be difficult to realize these savings. Framers around here just do not believe it's that much faster until they experience it. When comparing costs you need to take into consideration other things. Such as SIPS framed homes require a smaller HVAC unit than does a conventionally framed house. Also over 20 years utility costs are less than half with a SIPS framed house featuring 6" walls than a conventionally framed house.

Traditional Stick Framing

Traditional builders know and love traditional stick framing as the old standby method. Depending on what you compare it to, this can be the least expensive method, at least as far as materials are concerned. Most builders stick with traditional framing just because it's traditional. They know it and trust it. But that certainly does not mean it is the best way.

Traditional framing, commonly called stick framing, consists of using a lot of individual components assembled completely onsite. Floor joists are typically built from either 2x8's or 2x10's with limited spanning capabilities. Walls are 2x4's or 2x6's spaced 16 inches on center with a matching bottom plate and two matching top plates. Corners, windows and door ways are built up and reinforced with multiple components to carry roof loads.

I have several problems with traditional framing starting with overall quality. Dimensional lumber for floor joists like 2x8's and 2x10's require beams and supports with maximum spans for a 2x8 at 12 feet and the maximum span for a 2x10 at 14 feet. Now this book is not about engineering or lumber spans. You do not really need to know much about these spans. Here is what you do need to know:

- The limited span capability of dimensional lumber means some serious limitations in design.
- Using dimensional lumber will almost guarantee you will have squeaky floors somewhere. Some builders will tell you it's not a problem if done right, but that's BS and they know it.
- If dimensional lumber is used for floor joists, any plumbing and HVAC lines run under the floor have to go below the floor joists. Have you ever been in a basement or crawl space where the HVAC trunk line hangs 12 to 18 inches below the floor joists?
- There are a lot of parts and you are depending on a carpenter who may or may not understand spans, load factors, etc. Most building inspectors will catch it, though some may not.

Traditional framing spaces 2x4's and 2x6's at 16 inches on center in walls, leaving more room for air leaks and less room for insulation. Stick framing roofs add a significant amount of labor time, erasing a good portion of the savings gleaned from materials. Complicated roofs can add a ton of time to construction when stick framing. We've had stick framed roofs take four and five weeks to build just the roof. Let me tell you, there won't be any savings left after one of those projects.

Now you have probably noticed that I am not a big fan of traditional framing. I just do not see where there are any advantages. The only cost savings, in the end, are imaginary. Material savings are eaten up by increased labor costs. The quality is much lower, utility costs are going to be higher, and construction time increased. Man, what's not to love?

Subfloor

This applies to whatever framing method you may decide on. We used 3/4" plywood sub-flooring for the first couple of years I built homes. That was before we discovered Advantech® by Huber Engineered Woods®. We have since tried a couple of Advantech's® competitors but always went right back. Advantech® is an OSB (oriented strand board) product made with a better adhesive and lots of it. This product is far superior to anything else out there. It has a 50 year warranty, and unlike plywood and regular OSB, it can be rained on multiple times and not delaminate or swell. It is available in 3/4" and 5/8" thickness and comes in 4' x 8' sheets.

Don't just take my word for it though, do some research. You will find all but the most backward ass; old fashioned builders love the stuff. Make sure the builder glues it down and uses #10 ring shank nails. If you use the 5/8" see what Huber recommends. If installed properly you will not have a single squeak anywhere and the floor will last forever. If you hire a builder who is so old fashioned he wants to use plywood tell him to wake up. This is the 21st century for God's sake.

That reminds me of a couple of things I should mention. Residential builders and many of the trades tend to be extremely slow to embrace anything new. Engineered trusses for example took years to catch on with builders and framers; but like many of the other improvements in building technology; they are now viewed by all good builders as a superior product. Don't end up with an inferior home because you hired a dumbass builder still stuck in the 1960s. Also, when we first started building we would screw down all our sub-flooring. We did it because we wanted to avoid squeaks and produce a quality product. However, after a while we realized that a fair number of the screw heads would pop off, thus defeating the purpose. Using #10 ring shank nails has turned out to be a much better option.

Advanced Framing Techniques (O.V.E.)

After only a few houses, O.V.E. (Optimal Value Engineering) became my favorite way to frame. The quality is not as good as metal, the R-values are not as high as SIPS, and the framing crews are not as familiar with it as traditional methods, yet I consider it to be the most desirable method overall.

O.V.E. is a balance between lower upfront costs, overall quality, lower utility bills, faster construction and less waste. The only drawback is finding framers who are familiar with it. Advanced framing is kind of a misnomer because nothing could be simpler. It entails using engineered products that are assembled off site like floor trusses and roof trusses instead of dimensional lumber for these areas. Framing of walls use 2x6's, but they are spaced 24 inches on center instead of 16 inches on center. The extra spacing and using 2x6's instead of 2x4's lets us increase the R-value in the walls from R-11 to R-19. The extra space between studs results in more insulation overall.

I became a true believer after a conversation with the homeowner who purchased the first home we framed this way. With one electric heat pump on each of two floors and after a full year of use, the owner's highest electric bill had been $63. That's on a two story 2,200 square foot home. I have lived in apartments with higher electric bills.

To make this work everything is stacked on top of each other. For example, the wall studs (2x6's) are stacked over the floor trusses that are placed 24 inches on center also. The roof trusses are then placed directly over the 2x6 studs at 24 inches on center. Instead of two top plates, one is sufficient. Corners, windows, and doors require less lumber and everything is tied together with Advantech® sub-flooring, 7/16" OSB wall sheathing, and 5/8" roof sheathing. Framing material cost is less, but this is offset by higher costs for insulation and 5/8" drywall vs. 1/2" drywall. Both the costs of insulation and thicker drywall are offset in the future with lower utility bills. You do not have to use 5/8" drywall but I recommend it. Ceiling insulation is blown in to R-48 or higher.

There are additional upfront cost savings to be realized from framing labor and a smaller HVAC unit. However, framers who are not experienced with this method can be reluctant to discount a job the full value of their savings, because they often don't realize the full extent of those savings. Again, that's why it's important to find someone who is experienced in using more modern techniques vs. the "old school" type builders. All modern building codes allow for this type of framing and have for many years.

Chapter 3

Choosing and Hiring a Contractor

A building contractor was being paid by the week for a job that was likely to stretch over several months. He approached the owner of the property and held up the check he'd been given. "This is two hundred dollars less than we agreed on," he said.

"I know," the owner said, "But last week I overpaid you two hundred dollars, and you never complained."

The contractor said, "Well, I don't mind an occasional mistake. But when it gets to be a habit, I feel I have to call it to your attention." – blogspot.com/funnyjokes

Contractors often get a bad rap. Like lawyers or real estate agents, a few cause problems for all the rest. Most homebuilders are very decent, hardworking people who are more likely to be taken advantage of than the other way around. Ask any experienced homebuilder and they can give you multiple stories of clients who spent more than they could afford and wanted to stick the builder with the bill.

Now with that being said, there are some builders out there that fit the stereotype. As the homeowner it is your responsibility to do your due diligence and find one of the good ones. It is really not hard if you use your head, and above all, you are not trying to get something for nothing. Don't be like my friend's client who was lured away by a deal that was too good to be true. There is no such thing as something for nothing from a contractor, any more than from your business. It never ceases to amaze me how often I'll sell a home for $200,000 or so and the people act like I made $200,000 profit on them. Like my suppliers just gave me all the material and the subcontractors just did all the work as a favor to me, jeez give me a break.

If you have followed my earlier advice and figured out what you want and what is important up front, I promise it will make finding a good contractor much easier. In fact showing an experienced contractor you have a clue is the best way to get the best price available. Because they will know there is less chance you will be a major pain in the ass.

In a later chapter I am going to go over a few of the construction standards that are used to decide if construction is defective. One reason I want to include standards like these is to give you a gauge by which to judge the quality of construction. However, the main reason for inclusion is the hope you will understand that no house is perfect, nor will there ever be one. A new home has millions of parts and thousands of tasks involved, so perfection is impossible. That's just the way it is.

To illustrate, a few years ago I was asked by an attorney/neighbor to help with a lawsuit a client of his wanted to bring against another builder. I declined the offer several times because I did not want to be involved and because I was not enough of an expert to be a reliable witness. After several attempts to avoid the situation, I finally consented with an agreement I would not be asked to testify, but rather just help them know if they had a case.

These folks were so upset with their builder I was expecting the house to be a real mess. I took my superintendent with me to insure I didn't miss anything. Well there was nothing to miss. The concrete floor in the garage had hairline cracks where a few cracks had run out of the correctly cut expansion joints. Basically they were concerned about the same thing in the basement. Next they claimed a shoddy brick job because out of about 25,000 brick that were installed; they had searched and found 10 to 12 bricks with hairline cracks.

In addition, soil around the foundation had settled in a few places and a window had fogged up because of a broken seal which was a manufacturing defect. There were a few other minor things like nail pops but other than the window, there was not one thing wrong that was a defect. Everything else happens on every house ever built. Apparently the builder had offered to fix the window, the nail pops and the settling around the house; all standard procedure by a reputable builder. Of course, they were having none of it.

Unfortunately instead of trying to show the customer the list of possible defects that comes with every commercial home warranty, the builder just said to hell with it. We explained to my attorney friend and the homeowner nothing present was a defect. The manufacturer would replace the window. The settling of newly backfilled soil and hairline cracks in concrete were both normal. I suggested contacting the builder again and let him fix what was wrong. Yet once again all that happened was they got mad at me. All of it could have been avoided if someone had just bothered to check the facts.

In a similar incident, I was showing a spec home to an electrical engineer who complained he was living in a home built by a friend of mine. He said there were hairline cracks in several of the bricks and that my friend had refused to correct it. He didn't realize I knew the builder so I felt it was proper to explain what every sane person in the world understands. A few bricks with hairline cracks or even a few broken bricks out of thousands installed on a home made no difference. Every brick home ever built had the same situation and it meant nothing. Well he replied, "I'm an engineer and I know better". The fact he was an electrical engineer and not a structural engineer seemed to escape him. Anyway, when I later talked to my friend it turned out this had been going on for over a year. He had even offered to buy the house back from the guy just to make it go away. After that I quit returning the engineer's calls about my house until he gave up and went away.

The point of all this is put forth a lot of effort upfront to know what you are looking for and hire a reputable experienced builder. Then as Ronald Reagan said, "Trust but verify". Don't sweat over every little detail. You will get a quality home at a fair price, keep your sanity, and get loads of cooperation from your builder if something is wrong.

"I Can't Believe You Would Do Something So Vicious."
"You Forget My Dear; I Spent Two Years as a Building Contractor"
~ From The Movie Naked Gun 2 1/2.

Finding the Right Contractor

I have known a lot of builders over the years. Some have been unbelievably successful and others have been anything but successful. I have always felt we were somewhere in the middle. Most successful builders share some common characteristics; however those characteristics differ depending on what type of builder you're talking about.

Homebuilders are usually classified by the type of customer they cater to.

Custom Builder – This is the builder you are looking for to build your dream home. They build for a certain individual or family on a contract basis. With a custom builder, the client decides on the design of the home, how much will be spent, what products will be installed, specifications etc. If the client wants to use a certain subcontractor or do some of the work himself, the custom builder is fine with it as long as it's in the contract or a change order.

Semi-Custom Builder – Another option you might consider is a semi-custom builder. We have done a lot of this type work and it's probably my favorite after spec building. With semi-custom building the client will usually take a stock plan the builder has used before and make slight modifications to the plan. The customer has complete control over colors, flooring, type and brand of appliances, cabinetry and a long list of other options. What they don't control is the construction process. They don't have the right to choose subcontractors, type and quality of materials, etc. To clarify, in a purely semi-custom contract the client doesn't have those rights but nearly anything can be controlled by the contract as long as it's worked out up front. Keep in mind though; too many variations from the norm will diminish the advantages of semi-custom thus eliminating any cost savings. A true semi-custom builder will resist conceding much control of the construction process and major changes to a plan.

Speculative or Spec Builder –A spec builder will build a home with the express intent of selling it after completion, typically through a realtor. The spec builder will purchase a lot, pick a plan, make all the decisions about how the home is built and what materials and colors will be used. Pure spec builders are commonly small volume builders producing less than ten homes per year and building on scattered lots in different locations. The buyer ordinarily has little or no input in the building process. It's kind of a take it or leave it transaction. However if one were to find a spec home that suits their needs, this is usually a cheaper way to purchase, especially if you're dealing directly with the builder.

Production Builder –When you think of a production builder think of a factory. Most of the big national builders operate as production builders, producing hundreds or even thousands of homes a year. A production builder will generally offer between one and a dozen different plans at a standard base price for each plan with a limited amount of changes. Most offer some upgrades but they are limited in number and scope. The typical production builder is also the property developer, operating within a neighborhood or area. This is typically the cheapest way to purchase a new home.

Since this is a book mainly about custom building, my first recommendation is for you to only consider builders in the first two categories, either a custom or semi-custom builder. This means that you should not seriously consider a builder like me. A true custom or semi-custom builder builds this way exclusively. It's ok to use a builder that builds both semi-custom and custom but you should stay away from spec builders and production builders. That's not to say that spec and production people will necessarily do a poor job. Nonetheless, if you are interested in a true "have it your way" custom home, then you want someone who is used to dealing with and catering to people trying to build exactly what they want.

If I had it to do over I would never have built anyway except spec because that is what best suits my personality. I am not a particularly patient person with people that I don't agree with and that can be a real problem building custom homes. I say that because most successful spec and production builders are the same way. They are used to calling the shots, have a certain way of doing things, and don't always work and play well with others. I have a friend who is a super successful custom builder, but absolutely loses his shirt every time he attempts a spec home. I, on the other hand, love the process of building spec homes but tend to always have conflicts with custom home clients. Of course, that's not my fault!

So here's the point. If you want to be happy, get your way, end up with what you want, and have everyone still in love at the end, hire a contractor who has a successful track record building custom homes. Don't mess with people like me who only take on custom projects when specs aren't selling well.

Where to look

If you happen to be building in an area where you have spent many years, you may already know a good builder. If not, you probably know someone whose opinion you value that knows a good builder. Either way, don't stop there. Things aren't always as they seem. Sometimes a builder will appear to be successful and reputable, but when you dig a little deeper they may be broke and have not paid their suppliers in months. A common problem with builders is not following up on call backs. Some don't bother to carry proper insurance and some are hard to get along with. Many times a recommendation turns out to be the brother in law of whoever recommended them. If you're building in an area you're not familiar with you'll need to do some research just to get started. Below are some suggestions:

- Contact the local Homebuilders Association that's associated with the NAHB (National Association of Homebuilders). I am a member of our local association and I can honestly say I have never met a builder who was an active member and wasn't a "stand-up guy", honest, and quality minded. Bad builders don't bother with such things as a builders association. They are not concerned with improvement in quality, learning better ways to build, continuing education, or the enhancement of their reputation that membership provides. They typically "already know everything there is to know about homebuilding".
- Your local Chamber of Commerce can also be a good place to start your search for the same reason. Bad builders don't belong to the Chamber.
- That's not to say that all quality builders belong to these organizations, it's just that few bad builders do.

- Talk to suppliers like the sales reps from the lumber yards or plumbing and electrical suppliers.
- Talk to a local Realtors Association or a really successful realtor. You will know who they are because their signs are everywhere and billboards with their picture will be visible.
- Go and speak to mortgage loan officers at a couple of local banks or credit unions. They generally know several builders and certainly remember the ones who have caused problems for either the bank or its customers. Just don't mention my name.
- If you're moving into a subdivision, stop by and talk to a neighbor you see out working in the yard or going to the mailbox. It is amazing what these folks often know and will share with you.

These are of course not the only places to find a quality builder but they are a pretty good place to start. After you have the names of some recommended builders then you need to start doing a little research. This stage is a narrowing down stage. You will often have four to six names. Step one is to run those names by some of the people above, other than the one who provided the recommendation. You don't want to make a pest of yourself but one follow up inquiry won't be a problem. For your sake and sanity you should narrow this list down to three builders before you start contacting the builders themselves. Having too many builders looking to give you an estimate will drive you crazy.

A good place to start the culling process is to move any builder recommended more than once to the top of the

.st. Next move the builders who are members of the NAHB and or the Chamber of Commerce to the top. That will frequently do the trick but if you still need to reduce the candidates call their office and ask if they currently have any jobs under construction. If they do, go by and look at those jobs. It is best to go in the morning because it is when you will most likely see building activity. Look for signs that the site is clean and organized. Now don't expect a jobsite to be as neat as your living room. But it should be clear of scrap material spread all over the site. A couple of small scrap piles are actually a good thing, but if materials are spread far and wide that's a really bad sign. Do not actually go and talk to the subs, rather from the street observe if people seem to be working in a safe manner. You may not know all there is to know about safe practices but you will know very unsafe if you see it.

Is a worker moving his ladder like "John Belushi in Animal House" or is someone carrying large quantities of material on their back like a mule? You care about this for two reasons. One, these people will be working on your property and even though your builder is insured (they are, aren't they?); you do not want to increase the chances of someone being hurt on your property because of sloppy work habits. Two, a clean work site and attention to safety are signs your builder is a professional. By this point, you should be whittled down to three builders or less. If not, go ahead and contact everyone passing these tests.

Requirements to Trim the List Further

It's now time to start actually contacting the builders who survived the first cut. Below is a quick list of things you should request a builder to bring to your first meeting:

- **Proof of Insurance –** It is one thing to bend the rules a little or cut some corners, it's something quite different to screw up here. **Never ever** hire a contractor who does not have the full builder's insurance package. The builder's package should include workers compensation of at least $1,000,000, general liability of $2,000,000, and all their subs should carry both insurances also. General liability covers everyone in case someone not employed by the contractor gets hurt on the property. It is not necessary for them to have this at the first meeting, but before breaking ground, the builder should have in place a builder's risk policy that covers materials and labor for the full cost of the project, excluding land, in case of damage to the structure by wind, fire or some other disaster. Over the years I had two projects where I made a claim on builder's risk. One when a violent hail storm ruined a $25,000 roof and a $6,000 siding job on the same house; and the other when one of my guys ran a tele-handler (big outdoor forklift) over a completed septic system.
- **Copy of Contractors License–** Having a contractor's license doesn't guarantee a builder knows what they are doing, but in most jurisdictions it is illegal to build

without one. In some situations it is possible that you could be held liable for hiring an unlicensed builder. Regardless, any builder without a license is basically saying the rules don't apply to them. That's not who you want to be dealing with in building your home.

- **Two references–** Any experienced builder should be able to give you at least a couple names of people who like them. If not, you may want to reconsider.
- **A Local Business License –** Local authorities tend to take this pretty seriously. Like anything else where government is concerned, they get paid one way or the other. If your guy has not bothered to get one, not a good sign.
- **Supplier References –** You do not really need this at the first meeting but I would want to know the guy pays his bills before signing up.

Now you may be able to think of a few other things you would like to see before considering someone, but to me that should about cover it for now. Anyone left after meeting all these requirements is now eligible to provide an estimate or bid.

Bid or Estimate - A wild ass guess (WAG) carried out to two decimal places.

Low Bidder - A contractor who is wondering what he left out.

Engineer's Estimate - The cost of construction in heaven.

Getting Started

Before I get started on the finer points I would like to mention a couple of things about architects. These guys and gals are smart and necessary, but you need to keep them on a short leash. Do not be intimidated and always remember what it is you want. When working with an architect, don't forget these guys often have the attitude of an artist. Many think they are Frank Lloyd Wright and they want you to pay for their masterpiece.

Builders and architects often have difficult relationships. I do not want to say the builder is always innocent. Still, upon finding a mistake in the blueprints on a small commercial building, I was told by an architect, "I don't make mistakes".

"Yeah right," I said as I rained blows down upon him! Keep that true story in mind and don't be intimidated by their "superior intellect".

Ok, you have now prequalified everyone and you are ready to get down to the real deal. At this point you should have acquired your property and have a set of blueprints for the builder to study. I have found it works best to meet a potential client at their property for the first meeting. It works better for everyone because the builder needs to see what he or she is dealing with and you need to get their input on things to consider that you may not even be aware of.

When you supply blueprints to a builder you should bring five to ten copies to the first meeting. Sure it will cost you a little money, but most builders hate it when you ask them to spend their money on copies of your prints when they have no idea if they will get the job. For an accurate estimate the builder needs a copy for himself, the framing supplier, the electrical sub, the plumbing sub, the cabinetry people, the brick mason, the siding contractor, the roofer, the sheetrock sub, the painter, the flooring people and the concrete finisher. If there is a landscaping plan the landscaper needs to see a plan. These are the people who need to see a copy but not necessarily the people who need a copy.

I always like to get a copy to every sub involved because it makes it so much easier and faster to put together an estimate. I still have to get it to them, but when subs have a copy of the plan they will get all the estimates back to me on time, avoiding unnecessary delays. I can do a material takeoff and relay the quantities to them, but that makes me responsible for the accuracy. It's hard for them to blame mistakes on anyone else if they have a copy of the prints. Whenever it's time to pull permits, the building authorities will need between two to ten copies anyway, depending on the jurisdiction.

At this meeting you will develop your first impressions. While all first impressions aren't always accurate, strong first impressions usually are.

- Does the builder show up on time or if not, call and tell you they are running late?
- Does he or she look and act reasonably professional?
- Do their communications with you have a logical sequence or are they all over the place with their thoughts?

- Do they listen when you talk or are they busy telling you how much they know while frequently interrupting you? Do they impress you as being a know it all?
- Do they answer your questions or seem to intentionally avoid or discount them?
- Try to get a peek inside their vehicle. I once had the opportunity to spend a day with a very successful national builder who recruited other builders to partner with him. He complimented me on the interior of my truck being clean and not piled high with trash, samples and being generally unorganized. According to this guy, if a builder picked him up in a dirty truck (dirty inside not out), he immediately wrote them off. After dealing with hundreds of builders he realized that "any builder not caring enough about cleaning up his act for an important meeting would nine out of ten times not succeed with his company". These same builders had the same attitude with the customers and that rarely worked out. Now I'm not saying his truck should be spotless. Yet if they don't consider this meeting important enough to straighten up their truck, subsequent meetings will be even less important.

By far the most important element when picking a builder is compatibility. If you are uncomfortable with this person's personality now, it will only get worse. I have had two instances where I declined to proceed with a customer past the first meeting and a couple where I wish I had declined. In both cases that I declined, I later found they had been turned away by other local builders. In the cases where

I regretted taking the client's project, the signs of incompatibility were clear at the first meeting, but I ignored it to my frustration later. It is important you pay attention to this area. Depending on the size of your project, you will be dealing with this person from three months to over a year. If you dislike each other, it's going to be a tough row to hoe.

Plan Now, Be Happy Later.

One of the first custom homes I built was for a couple who always took forever to make up their mind about anything. They never wanted to get specific about anything except the price. They always wanted to "ballpark" everything. I would give them a price, then they would come back with something completely different and when I redid the quote (many times) they would complain I was always raising the price. That was the last time that happened.

As I mentioned before, now is the time to work out all the details. Don't be so anxious to get started, you fail to give the builder what he needs to give you an accurate estimate. When you come to the first meeting have your plan tweaked to what you want. Bring a specification sheet that lists all the particulars on cabinets, flooring, countertops, appliances, plumbing fixtures, type of water heater (traditional or tank less), type of HVAC (gas, electric etc.). What decking material do you want to use (wood, composite, concrete, etc.)? How will the foundation be constructed?

At this point know whether you want brick or siding, asphalt, or metal roofing, etc. Estimating the size requirements for HVAC and other systems along with material quantities is the builder's responsibility, but it is your responsibility to know types and particular brands and to have that available at the meeting where the plans are delivered. There have been a few times I have lost projects because folks were in a huge hurry to get an estimate. An estimate without details is the ultimate WAG .You don't have to take my word for it. A lot of people don't. But in every case I know where people ignored this advice, the projects were always over budget and/or underfunded. Banks base your loan request on the figures you give them (they usually have some guidelines but they're mostly not even close).

Ok, we've found three builders who meet our requirements. You have given them what they need to make an accurate estimate. Depending on how busy they are, it should take no more than one to two weeks to provide you with a detailed estimate. If it is more than a couple of weeks, more often than not, they are too busy to give you the service you deserve.

You now have three estimates with all your specifications included in the price, right? Now consider the definition of the low bidder (a contractor wondering what he left out) and disregard the low bid. Most of the time, the low bidder did miss something. However the oldest trick in construction is intentionally estimating a bid low, get the job, and make it up with change orders. **If you are such a moron to fall for a price significantly lower than the other two bids, you are guaranteed to get screwed and you deserve it.**

When you get the estimate, take the time to go [illegible]h the details (if it's not detailed, send it back). Make [illegible]l your specifications are addressed. In a later chapter I am going to go through the construction phases and even give you some formulas so you will have an idea if they have padded the numbers too much. But for now just make sure it is a detailed estimate and all your specs are addressed. Whoever did the best job of covering all the bases is the guy you want to hire, even if he is a little higher. Often a little difference can be negotiated down, but remember your main goals are twofold. Finding a competent, honest builder and eliminating as many surprises as possible. At this point you pick the contractor and you are ready to start negotiating the contract. The next chapter will present the most common types of construction contracts and give you some of the pros and cons of each type.

Chapter 4

Common Construction Contracts

Types and Considerations

An agreement between the owner and contractor in which the contractor agrees to construct the owner's building (or other described project) in accordance with the contract documents and within a specified time, for a mutually-agreed upon consideration to be paid by the owner.
~ McGraw-Hill Dictionary of Architecture and Construction.

The definition above is a good place to start but in practice, construction contracts are routinely highly customized documents. A well done contract is as unique as the project it covers. Below are some common types of contracts categorized by how charges are accrued and paid. After a brief description of both, we will talk about some advantages, disadvantages, and my opinion of contracts in general.

- **UNIT PRICE (ITEM WISE) CONTRACT–** An al a carte type of agreement where the type of materials, the tasks involved, and the price for each unit have been determined but the final quantities are not. In residential construction, this type of contract would mostly be used in a remodel. It often involves an architect who oversees the project, verifies quantities used, and approves all charges before the contractor is reimbursed. Rarely used in residential construction or remodeling because of the expense of hiring an architect and the cost of keeping up with so many different items. It can be good for the owner because only items actually installed are paid for and the architect is responsible for maintaining quality of the work. The contractor invests his own money up front and is reimbursed on pre-scheduled draws. I don't recommend it because this type of contract is complicated, expensive, and the same advantages can be obtained by other forms of a contract.

- **LUMP SUM (FIRM FIXED PRICE) CONTRACT–**A lump sum contract is the most common type of contract and the one an average person would be most familiar with. In a fixed price contract the contractor and client agree on an exact price. The trouble with this type of arrangement is the exact price is seldom exact. In a lump sum contract the contractor will take the customers plan and spec sheet (most people rarely supply a spec sheet) and use that to create an estimate. The real trouble often comes when the client doesn't understand that changes to the scope of work or materials changes the contract. Most people wrongly assume once they get a price they can make minor changes without changing that price. Secondly; the lump sum contract is by far the most expensive way to build.

The only times I've had problems and disagreements with clients have been over lump sum contracts. I always do my best to explain to clients, before we sign a contact, how an estimated price is based on the information they provide. I'll always stand behind any price I provide as long as we don't make changes or run into things that can't be predicted like rock. That's why I spend so much time stressing the importance of getting all the details correct up front. With some clients it's like they never heard anything we discussed, never read the contract, and had never been involved in a business transaction before. The following is a true story that illustrates the kinds of problems that can be incurred, with a fixed sum contract, when people fail to stick to the plan.

But You Said It Was Only Going to Cost $260,000.

One of my favorite ways to build is using a building system package. I'll explain later about the different building systems and my take on each type. For this particular project we used a complete package from a panelized building manufacturer. With a panelized system the framing is assembled in a factory, shipped to the site in pieces, and assembled onsite with the aid of a crane attached to the truck used to ship the pieces. The truck has an enclosed trailer covered with a removable tarp. With the tarp removed the crane will reach into the trailer and pull out large wall sections and roof sections where they are set on the subfloor and nailed in place. The beauty of this system is any house under 3,000 square feet can be framed completely and ready for the shingles in one full workday (8-12 hours).The material for the entire house, with the exception of brick and flooring, is shipped in two shipments. Building a home this way is specifically designed to help insure all the decisions are made up front and everything is onsite just in time. Doing it this way allows the builder to take advantage of the manufacturer's buying power, reduces shipping costs and generates less framing labor. Unfortunately this was not exactly how it worked out with these clients.

"You do understand this will screw up the whole system if you make these changes" I said.

"The contract we agreed to was to use the entire panelized system. You chose the siding and you picked out the cabinets. The cabinet change alone will add $18,000 to the cost and there is no room in the future assemblies to make that up. We kept the cost down by going with the package. All the changes you have asked for will end up costing between $25,000 to $30,000".

"We know," they said. "We really like this new siding better and the panelized people don't offer that color. And I just love, love, love these new cabinets," the wife said.

"I understand but if you decide to do this, I will have to have a change order to reflect the added cost," I told her.

"That's OK," he said "She wants what she wants".

Well, as you've probably guessed, all that was important was she gets what she wants (until the bill comes due).This couple had applied for a construction loan for $260,000, the exact amount of the contract. The project was now $28,000 over budget and the bank was balking over the added expense. Neither I nor the client had disclosed the change order to the bank. In hindsight that was probably my fault, but it's not actually my place or responsibility to deal with their bank. Now guess what they said.

"You told us this house was only going to cost $260,000. Now it's $28,000 over and we don't have the money. The bank doesn't want to loan us the extra money so what are you going to do about this?"

With all the control I could muster, I said. “I’m going to take this change order to the bank and explain to them if you don’t pay me or they don’t pay me I am going to put a lien on this house and you won’t be moving in. You can blame me all you want but you and I both know I warned you about this before we signed the contract, and again before we did the change order.”

In the end the bank loaned them the extra money, but not before I had to listen to a week or more of crying and belly aching about how I should have known all this would happen. To this day these folks still don’t like me. I have to say there is no love lost. What a couple of dip wads.

There are several lessons to be learned from this story. One is apparently I’m a dumbass. In addition it’s important to note a fixed cost lump sum contract can end up causing a lot of problems. It is very important to be realistic about what you want <u>before</u> you sign this type of contract. If you do use a lump sum contract always get approved for a bigger loan than the contract amount or have the money set aside for the difference (20% is a good number to start).

Please don’t put yourself in the position the couple above ran into. You can blame it on the contractor till the cows come home, but if you run out of money it will still be a big problem for you. The last thing to remember is that a fixed price contract is the most expensive type of contract. Because the builder absolutely <u>must</u> add in extra funds in his contract to allow for contingencies that may or may not happen. If they don’t happen he is not going to give you back that money, nor should he. He took the risk and he should get the reward. Just so you know, deciding you want more expensive cabinets is not a contingency a builder would be responsible for.

- **LABOR CONTRACT –** This is the way I built my own house. Since I'm a contractor I already had accounts set up with suppliers and already knew subcontractors to do the actual work, so it worked out great for me. I just ordered the materials, had the materials delivered as they were needed and scheduled the subs as needed.

  For the typical homeowner though this can be a little tricky. The way this arrangement works is the homeowner will pretty much act as his or her own contractor. They will decide what materials to order, schedule out deliveries and schedule the labor or subs. This would require the homeowner to have the free time to devote to this very time consuming process and possess a pretty thorough knowledge of the entire operation. The homeowner just contracts directly with each supplier and each sub.

  At first glance it would appear a labor contract would save the entire 20 – 25% that would typically be paid to a contractor. However, not all is as it appears. A contractor's price is not all profit. In most contracts a good portion of the contractors share is overhead. The majority of overhead is made up of expenses that will be incurred, no matter who assumes the role of contractor. If the homeowner uses their vehicle to do the "running around" that must be done, they would still incur the same expenses of fuel, auto insurance, and wear and tear on the vehicle a contractor would. In both cases workers compensation insurance, general liability insurance, and builders risk insurance are all required.

Regardless of who assumes the contractor's role the risks inherent in the construction process are still there. Unless the homeowner considers their own time worthless, resources have to be allocated for that time. One should also consider these facts, suppliers and sub-contractors don't value a one off deal with a single homeowner anywhere near as much as they value a relationship with a contractor. The contractor is a potential source for future business and the single homeowner is not. Therefore the homeowner is going to pay higher prices, experience more delays, and in general receive less quality customer service than a contractor would.

Like I mentioned before, if a sub has a regular customer calling who needs something done quickly, he will almost always pull off a homeowner's job to accommodate a contractor. It may not seem fair but it's just the way it is. So the point is you don't save nearly as much money as it may seem at first glance.

One way to mitigate some of the disadvantages of this contract is to pay a contractor to handle part of the responsibilities, although this is better handled using one of the last two types of contracts.

- **Cost Plus Contract –**I like building on a cost plus contract because it works great for everyone involved. The contractor, in this case, handles everything pretty much as he would in a fixed price (lump sum) contract. The contractor incurs the costs by purchasing the materials and paying the subs and other expenses. He is then reimbursed at the end of each phase by a preset draw system, the same way as in a fixed contract. The big difference is the contractor doesn't mark up anything. He or she simply presents the invoices incurred during the phase with the draw request. The homeowner reimburses them for that amount plus a fixed predetermined amount for the contractor's services. Usually a percentage of the construction costs.

Let's say for example you and I have a cost plus contract for a home we have estimated will cost $240,000. I agree to provide my services for 10% or $24,000, for a total of $260,000. That means you have agreed to pay all the costs involved, including overhead like insurance etc., but only the actual cost incurred. In addition you will pay me the $24,000 split over each draw. Depending on the size and cost of the process, there are typically 5 – 10 scheduled draws in a contract. We will take 5 draws for this project. For a project this size, I would typically get my first draw after the completion of the initial excavation, surveying, basement walls, basement slab and waterproofing. In other words, when the foundation is complete and framing is ready to start on the main house. That is normally about 25% of the project cost. So the draw request would be for

$240,000 x .25 = $60,000 + 1/5th of $24,000 = $4,800 for a total draw request of $64,800.

At this point you would either write me a check or take the draw request to your bank. I would expect your bank to fund the request within three business days; at which point I would supply you with a partial lien release (more later) for $64,800. There will actually be, let's say, five partial lien releases, one from me, one from the surveyor, one from the excavator, one from the foundation wall contractor and one from the concrete company. These lien releases are important for you because they are proof that everyone involved in the process to this point has been paid.

As the project moves along there will be four more draw requests with the last one paid when the project is complete and all lien releases have been signed.

This is a great way to build a house if you've done your homework and found an honest builder. You then need to go through the bills at each draw. Do they match the estimate? Do they make sense? The point is, unless you have hired a crook and haven't paid any attention at all, this is one of the more inexpensive ways to build because you are only paying for what you are getting. It is also a pretty good way to control the costs because you know where you stand, compared to the estimate, after each phase.

- **PROJECT MANAGMENT CONTRACT**–This is bar none my favorite way to build. It can be difficult to pull off if your financing because most bank loan officers don't understand it. Of course if it was always a requirement for a banker to understand something, very little would ever get done.

In a project management agreement, the client sets up his own accounts with suppliers and pays the suppliers and sub-contractors directly. The contractor is responsible for managing the entire project, from determining material quantities, to managing and scheduling deliveries and subcontractors, to obtaining insurance and managing safety. In essence it's just a cost plus contract with a couple of major differences. First, it removes almost all of the risk for the contractor because he is not responsible for paying the bills. If you don't pay your supplier he's not responsible. That makes it much easier for a contractor to work on a much smaller margin because of the massive reduction in risk. For the contractor the only thing at risk is his or her time. Though it would be super painful to not get paid, it would not ruin a builder's business or hurt unpaid supplier relationships. To earn their management fee, the contractor is still responsible to the homeowner to look out for their best interest, control costs, obtain lien waivers, and perform every other responsibility he would have with any other type of contract, except financial responsibility.

For the homeowner, the advantages are numerous. This is by far the least expensive way to build a home without doing the work or completely managing the project yourself. The contractor can and will work for less. The subs and suppliers will offer the homeowner the same pricing because they're still working with and for the contractor. The homeowner's only responsibility is to pay the bills on time. That's their responsibility anyway.

Now before you assume I'm blowing smoke up your skirt, there are a couple of disadvantages to the homeowner in building with a project management contract. First and foremost, the homeowner must have enough cash on hand to pay the bills between draws if financing, or have easy access to cash if paying them directly. You also need to either be available to write checks to subcontractors every Friday or have someone else available to do it for you. Suppliers need to be paid in full at least once a month with some sooner than that. If however these issues are not a problem for a homeowner, the savings will be significant. For example, I built a home a couple of years ago for one of my best friends. For his $380,000 house, I managed the entire project over a seven month period for about $15,000. While I probably would not have done it that cheap for a stranger, I wouldn't have needed to charge a lot more to be happy. For a comparison, my fee including overhead for this project on a lump sum contract would be between 20% and 25% or $76,000 to $95,000. Now 100% of the difference would not be savings because there would still be workman's comp premiums and general liability premiums, but there would be no markup. As long as the contractor uses only insured subcontractors then the cost of insurance premiums would be very low because these premiums are charged according to payroll costs (more later).

Other Considerations and My Opinions

Before I finish up the discussion on contracts I would like to briefly discuss financing. Banks and Mortgage Companies SUCK! They are pretty much a bunch of good for nothings that slow down the entire process and they act like they are doing you a favor. They rarely have a clue about the building process and usually want to dictate draws based on worksheets developed by some snot-nosed MBA who has never stepped foot on a construction site.

Never assume a bank or Mortgage Company is doing you a favor loaning you money. Their business is selling money; like my business is selling management services, and the suppliers business is selling building supplies, nothing more. They generally are not capable of rational thought. They operate solely on ratios developed years ago that may or may not be relevant today.

I have seen them leave homeowners twisting in the wind just to be a jackass and they only hang around if you don't really need them. They sure won't be there if you really need them. Other than that they're great, and I love'em! Now I know for most of us, we need a source of financing to build a custom home. I'm just saying do not let them push you around and if possible avoid them like the plague.

Let me explain a couple of other things in a little more depth:

Lien Waivers or Releases – I earlier mentioned something called a lien release, often called a lien waiver. These are very important to a homeowner. Many builders don't like using them because it is kind of a pain in the ass to have to run around getting these things signed, but don't let anyone talk you out of using them. A lien waiver is a form (ask your attorney for one) that everyone who performs work or supplies materials on your project should sign every time they get paid. There may be more but I am familiar with and use two types.

- **Partial Lien Release** – Most suppliers and subs on your project will be due multiple payments. When a supplier or sub delivers materials or services for your project and you are paying them now for work they have completed, but they will provide more goods or services in the future, you need them to sign a partial lien release. This simply acknowledges they have been paid for part of their contract and they waive any right to place a mechanics lien on your property for that amount.

  For example; the electrician will most often give you or your contractor two invoices, one after they complete the rough-in and one when they complete all of their work. Let's say the contract is

$6,000 paid ½ at rough-in and ½ at completion. When you pay the rough-in invoice you need a partial lien release from three people, the electrical sub, the sub's supplier that provided the wire and other materials and the general contractor. When the electrical sub has completed all of his work on the project, you will need a final lien waiver upon completion from all three for that invoice.

- **Final Lien Release –**Using the electrician example again, the final lien release will need to be signed when the electrician has completed and been paid for all of the work he will do on your project. At this point the electrical sub and his supplier will sign a final release acknowledging payment in full for their entire contract and the contractor will sign a partial release for the amount paid to the electrician. The contractor will usually sign a partial release for all the money he collects at each draw and that release will cover the money paid to the electrician. At the end of the project, when everyone has been paid you should have a final lien release from anyone who supplied materials or had a contract or sub-contract to work on your property.

In East Tennessee a lot of builders don't like using lien waivers because they like doing things the "good ole boy way". But you need to remember it's the "good ole boy" that ends up nailing you. The number one way homeowners end up getting nailed by contractors and their subs is by paying someone for a job and then that someone doesn't pay their supplier. A custom home is expensive enough without paying for things twice.

Another thing I need to mention about contracts is you should never sign the contractor's version of a contract or proposal without having an attorney hired by you to look over it. So many people have lost money or suffered in some other way because they were too cheap to pay a lawyer a few hundred dollars to protect their interests. While most contractors are honest hardworking people, even the best of us with good intentions are going to have standard contracts that at least slightly favor ourselves. The trick is to make sure it is "fair" to all involved. A good attorney with experience in construction law will know what is "fair" and whether the contract is too much in the contractors favor. Your lawyer will rarely need to rewrite the entire contract but can point out what needs to be changed to protect you.

Finally, make sure that the contract is tied to the drawings and your specification sheet (you provided one, right?). Don't sign a contract that is tied to the builders proposal but instead the contract should be tied to your drawings. It's really beyond the scope of this book to describe all the finer points in detail (that's your lawyer's job). For now it's enough to say the last thing you want is to be constantly hearing, "well now that wasn't in my bid". My price included $3.00 per yard linoleum not that fancy tile you wanted.

And let me warn you now. If it's not spelled out what you want in the contract documents you will hear that crap often. Builders are always afraid of bidding a project too high and losing the job. So if you do not spell out what you want, you will either have to settle for what the builder bid on or be prepared to pay through the nose.

Change orders and extras always cost more than what they would have cost in the original quote, ALWAYS!

Chapter 5

The Construction Process

In this chapter I am going to give you a general feeling of the overall construction process. What I'm not going to do is attempt to make you an expert on construction assemblies and bore you to death with a lot of details you have no need to know. After all, I'm not trying to teach you to be a contractor. But I am trying to make sure you don't get nailed by a bad one. I also want to do my best to make sure this is a fun, enjoyable experience for you and that you are happy with the end result.

I have thought long and hard about this chapter, trying to decide on the best way to cover what you need to know without boring you to death. I finally decided to do a checklist showing the basic steps to building with four different systems: the traditional or stick built approach, the metal framing approach, the panelized approach, and the modular approach. I will add some suggestions and a few things to watch if I feel you need to pay attention to them.

I will end this chapter with a few formulas that will give you an idea how material quantities are derived from your drawings, not so you can figure all the exact quantities but so if a number sounds a little squirrelly or way too high you can run a few numbers to see if they make sense. Feel free to scan through this chapter and skip anything that doesn't apply to you. That's why I did it in checklist fashion, to make it easy to skip through and ignore if you so choose. Keep in mind also this is the way I organize these building systems. If your builder varies the process a little it doesn't mean he's doing anything wrong. This will give you a general idea of the process. Assume a full basement for all systems.

Traditional or Stick Framing Checklist

1. Purchase Property – I prefer this to be the first step because it makes the design process more accurate and complete. Also do any testing at this stage, preferably before you purchase, like a perk test report, soils report or any test you feel is necessary.
2. Set a Preliminary Budget – This does not have to be exact at this point but within a range.
3. Start Shopping for Financing (if applicable) – You may want to get prequalified for a loan and a rate. No need to design a mansion if you can't fund it.
4. Design or Purchase a House Plan – You may or may not need an architect.
5. Put Together a Specification Sheet – Be realistic and specific about what you want. Do you want stainless appliances, concrete walls in the basement or a block crawl space, Kohler plumbing fixtures, crown molding, gas heat or a heat pump, etc.? Now is the time to make these decisions and put them in writing.
6. Start Your Contractor Search – Review the steps in chapter 3 and whittle your choices down to three bidders.
7. Hire an Attorney – I would want to do this before choosing a builder because he may know if the builder you like has had problems. Hire an attorney with experience in construction law.
8. Get Three Bids and Pick Your Contractor – Remember you rarely want to hire the low bidder. When you ask each contractor for a bid ask them to

include a copy of their standard contract and what type of contract they prefer. Remember there should be some rapport. Make sure you pick a contract type you're comfortable with and let the builder know your requirements like lien waivers etc. Have them agree to keep the site clean as it progresses. I have seen construction sites so filthy and piled up that it was dangerous.

9. Take The Contract to Your Lawyer for Review – Now, now, don't skip this part!
10. Get Financing Approval from the Bank (if applicable). Finalize the budget.
11. Sign the Contract – Find out who the contractor will use for suppliers and subs and contact them to inform them who you are and tell them to keep you informed about payments etc. (This is not necessary if you're paying the bills).
12. Meet with Your Builder and the Surveyor at Your Site – They will assist you with proper orientation, placement issues, and things to be aware of like where septic lines or sewer lines must go, etc. Have the surveyor lay out the property lines and the preliminary house corners.
13. Apply For and Receive Permits – Now you're ready to break ground!
14. Foundation Excavation – If there's a basement there should be a three foot over- dig to allow for working behind the walls for waterproofing. Soil from excavation should be stockpiled on site.
15. Surveyor to Set Corners to Dig Footings
16. Set Temporary Electric Pole and Have Water Meter Set.

17. Excavator Digs Footings Per Code – Footings for house, garages, retaining walls etc. are dug all at once.
18. Footer Inspection Per Code
19. Plumber Installs Exit Pipe Under Footing
20. Concrete Footing Poured Per Code
21. Surveyors Sets All Corner Pins
22. Foundation Walls and Retaining Walls Erected Per Code (Anchor bolts are also placed)
23. Foundation Walls Waterproofed and Foundation Drains Placed
24. Foundation Inspection (if applicable)
25. Place 4 – 6 Inches of Gravel for Slab (if basement only).
26. Pretreat for Termites (some places do this before placing gravel).
27. Rough-in Plumbing Per Plan and Code
28. Order Floor and Roof Trusses
29. Cover Gravel with 6 mil Poly Vapor Barrier
30. Place Slab Expansion Joints on Foundation Walls (if applicable)
31. Pour Concrete Slabs (basement only)
32. Seal Concrete Slabs (same day as pour)
33. Order Framing Lumber Package and Bathtub and Shower Units
34. Cut Expansion Joints in Slabs (within 24 hours of pour)
35. Slab Inspection (if applicable)
36. Install Sill Plates and Sill Sealer
37. Frame any Basement Walls (if applicable)
38. Set Floor Trusses
39. Install Advantech® Subfloor

40. You Can Now Backfill Against the Basement Walls (Use # 57 stone 2 feet deep & drain tile)
41. Set Bath and Shower Units
42. Frame First Floor Walls (and 2nd if applicable)
43. Frame Stairways (rough)
44. Set Roof Trusses
45. Install Roof Decking and Roofing Underlayment (30 lb. roofing felt or better)
46. Install Windows and Exterior Doors
47. Framing Inspection
48. Install Roofing
49. Plumbing Rough-in (Be sure they do a pressure test for at least 24 hours before inspection)
50. Electrical Rough-in (Additionally, rough-in extras like alarm systems or wall vacuums)
51. HVAC Rough-in
52. Plumbing and Electrical Rough-in Inspection
53. Have Permanent Electricity Hooked Up (Not all electric companies will do it this early but it's great if they will)
54. Install Wall Insulation
55. Start Exterior Siding (brick, stone, siding etc.)
56. Install Sheetrock
57. Finish Sheetrock
58. Order Cabinets and Trim
59. Primer on Sheetrock – I know contractors who do not believe in priming sheetrock saying 2 coats of paint are sufficient. Priming is the most important thing you can do for painting. You can put 5 coats on an unprimed wall and it will still leave shadows. I first discovered this fact when I was repainting the first

house I ever lived in. Coat after coat was just sucked right into the walls. Also use tinted primer.

60. Two Coats of Paint – If you decide on real deep colors (like Candy Apple Red) be prepared for several coats.
61. Hang Interior Doors and Trim (Cabinets, Vanities, etc.)
62. Paint Two Coats on Interior Trim (prime first if not pre-primed).
63. Should Be About to Complete Exterior Siding, Brick Etc.
64. Do Exterior Trim – Soffit, Metal, Gutters and Shutters etc.
65. You Can Place Blow-in Attic Insulation Any Time After This (Should be at least R-48)
66. Place All Exterior Concrete (walkways, driveways and porches etc.)
67. Seed and Straw Yard and Install Landscaping.
68. Build Decks
69. Install floors in kitchen and baths.
70. Deliver lighting, plumbing fixtures, and appliances.
71. Finish Electrical Work – Lights, appliances etc. Finish Electrical Work – Hanging lights, receptacle covers etc.
72. Do Final HVAC – Setting Units, installing grills & filters etc.
73. Final Inspections Electrical and HVAC
74. Set Plumbing Fixtures
75. Final Plumbing Inspection
76. Do Interior Punch List
77. Install Wood Floors (Some builders try to do flooring earlier. Don't let them because some dumbass will

come through the house with mud on his feet and gravel stuck in the mud ruining your floor.)

78. Install Carpets (Be sure the contractor cleans the floor very well before carpet is laid. My carpet guy says he sometimes has to sweep up trash, mud and other crap before he can start. If you put carpet on a filthy floor it will always be filthy.)
79. Final Cleanup
80. Exterior Punch List
81. Final Inspection If Required.
82. You're Ready to Move In.

Obviously a lot of this stuff can be done simultaneously. You don't have to wait on all the exterior stuff to be done before starting interior work. This is the way I do it and it works great. I'm including this to give you an idea what to expect. All contractors have their own system but it will be reasonably close to this list. You certainly don't need to follow your builder around telling him he's doing it wrong. However it is important that you pay attention to the suggestions I provide at some of the phases. If I wrote something extra (like cleaning the floor in step 78) it's because I've had a bad experience or known someone who has. Some contractors can be good builders but tend to do certain things half ass. Pay attention to my suggestions and you will be pleased you did.

Advanced Framing or O.V.E.: (Optimal Value Engineering)

In chapter two, I gave a pretty decent description of O.V.E. and all the advantages. As far as a checklist goes, it is exactly like the checklist for traditional framing above so there's no need to repeat it. Just the same I will give you a quick run through of the differences that are mostly in the framing and insulation phases.

- In traditional framing you have the option to use dimensional lumber like 2x10's or 2x12's for floor joists and stick framing the roof. Advanced framing always uses engineered floor trusses and roof trusses.
- The walls in O.V.E. use 2x6's instead of 2x4's and are spaced at 24 inches on center instead of 16 inches.
- The entire assembly is stacked on top of each other with the 2x6 wall studs directly over the floor trusses and the roof trusses exactly over the wall studs; again everything is spaced 24 inches on center.
- Insulation is increased to R-19 instead of R-11 or R-13 as with 2x4 studs at 16 inches on center. Because of the extra space between studs, more of the walls are covered with insulation significantly lowering utilities.
- You don't absolutely have to, but I like to use 5/8 inch roof decking and 5/8 inch sheetrock. By doing this and strapping down the floor trusses, the entire assembly is stronger thus less susceptible to wind damage.

Framing With Metal; Engineered Metal Packages and Metal Studs

I am going to skip over all the earliest steps (steps 1-35) to the completion of the foundation because that is pretty much the same on each method we use. The only early stage that is different is in the design phase and I'll start there.

1. With metal framing, before you go to see an architect, research and find a metal frame manufacture you may want to use. The process should be similar to finding a builder. Most companies doing this kind of work have designers on staff and that would save you money on an architect. If you do use an architect, the building will still have to be engineered by the manufacturer so it might save you a step.
2. Once all the drawings are finished take them to the local building inspector's office to head off any issues. In most states the metal framing manufacturer submits the finished drawing to a state agency. If the state agency approves the drawing, that will supersede the local building authority. Still, it's a smart move to pay your respects to the local inspector's office so not to unnecessarily step on any toes or wound anyone's pride.
3. You won't be able to use just any framing crew. You will have to hire a company that specializes in metal framing. Of course that's your builder's problem. I'm just making you aware.
4. Install Sill Plates and Sill Sealer
5. Frame any Basement Walls (if applicable)
6. Set Floor Trusses (metal, designed by metal manufacturer)
7. Install Advantech® Subfloor

8. You Can Now Backfill Against the Basement Walls (Use #57 stone 2' deep & drain tile)
9. Set Bath and Shower Units
10. Frame First Floor Walls (and 2nd if applicable)
11. Frame Stairways (rough)
12. Set Roof Trusses (metal, designed by manufacturer)
13. Install Roof Decking and Roofing Underlayment (30 lb. roofing felt or better)
14. Install Windows and Exterior Doors
15. Framing Inspection (according to approved state drawings)
16. Install Roofing
17. Plumbing Rough-in (Be sure they do a pressure test for at least 24 hours before inspection). You should get a slight discount because there are no holes needing to be drilled.
18. Electrical Rough-in (In addition, rough-in extras like alarm systems or wall vacuums).You should get the same discount here as plumbing rough-in.
19. HVAC Rough-in
20. Plumbing and Electrical Rough-in Inspection
21. Have Permanent Electricity Hooked Up (Not all electric companies will do it this early, but it's great if they will).
22. Install Wall Insulation (Add foam insulation board under OSB sheeting to make up for R-value loss from metal).
23. Start Exterior Siding (brick, stone, siding etc.)

24. Install Sheetrock (must be 5/8 inch sheetrock and all self-tapping metal screws)
25. Finish Sheetrock
26. Order Cabinets and Trim (with metal framing this can be done earlier because all walls are perfectly straight and plumb).
27. Primer on Sheetrock – I know contractors who don't believe in priming sheetrock saying 2 coats of paint are sufficient. Priming is the most important thing you can do for painting. You can put 5 coats on an unprimed wall and it will still leave shadows. I first discovered this fact when I was repainting the first house I ever lived in. Coat after coat was just sucked right into the walls. Also use tinted primer.
28. Two Coats of Paint – If you decide on real deep colors (like Candy Apple Red) be prepared for several coats.
29. Hang Interior Doors and Trim (Cabinets, Vanities etc.)
30. Paint Two Coats on Interior Trim (prime first if not pre-primed)
31. Should Be About to Complete Exterior Siding, Brick etc.
32. Do Exterior Trim – Soffit, Metal, Gutters and Shutters etc.
33. You Can Place Blow-in Attic Insulation Any Time After This (Should be at least R-48)
34. Place All Exterior Concrete (walkways, driveways and porches etc.)
35. Seed and Straw Yard and Install Landscaping.
36. Build Decks

37. Install floors in kitchen and baths.
38. Deliver lighting, plumbing fixtures and appliances.
39. Finish Electrical Work – Lights, appliances etc. Finish Electrical Work – Hanging lights, receptacle covers etc.
40. Do Final HVAC – Setting Units, installing grills & filters etc.
41. Final Inspections Electrical and HVAC
42. Set Plumbing Fixtures
43. Final Plumbing Inspection
44. Do Interior Punch List
45. Install Wood Floors (Some builders try to do flooring earlier. Don't let them because some dumbass will come through the house with mud on his feet and gravel stuck in the mud ruining your floor.)
46. Install Carpets (be sure the contractor cleans the floor very well before carpet is laid. My carpet guy says he sometimes has to sweep up trash, mud and other crap before he can start. If you put carpet on a filthy floor it will always be filthy.)
47. Final Cleanup
48. Exterior Punch List
49. Final Inspection If Required.
50. You're Ready to Move In.

Structural Insulated Panels (SIPS)

Again I'm going to skip the first steps (1-35) because the early steps to basement completion are the same.

Really about the only real change with SIPs is that you send the SIPs Company the plans early and they do custom drawings for you that coincide with the numbers printed on each panel. The whole system consists of a set by numbers system with each wall panel set by the number assigned to it on the drawing. Each panel comes with conduit for plumbing and electric already installed so if a wall calls for a light switch, cable box, receptacle or plumbing pipe, the box or pipe is installed at the factory. This saves work for both the electrician and the plumber which should save money for each trade. They also are set really fast, making it possible to frame the entire house in 2 days or less. Of course you also have completely eliminated the insulation step because both the wall and roof panels are already insulated.

1. Take Drawings to SIPs Manufacturer about Two to Four Weeks Before Permitting.
2. Take The Finished Drawing to the Building Inspector Early in Case They Are Not Familiar With the Process.
3. Install Sill Plates and Sill Sealer
4. Frame any Basement Walls (if applicable)
5. Set Floor Trusses
6. Install Advantech® Subfloor
7. You Can Now Backfill Against the Basement Walls. (use # 57 stone 2' deep & drain tile)
8. Set Bath and Shower Units
9. Frame First Floor Walls (and 2nd if applicable) SIPs are set according to layout. Interior non-load bearing walls are stick framed.
10. Frame Stairways (rough)
11. Set Roof Trusses

12. Install Roof Decking and Roofing Underlayment (30 lb. roofing felt or better)
13. Install Windows and Exterior Doors
14. Framing Inspection
15. Install Roofing
16. Plumbing Rough-in (Be sure they do a pressure test for at least 24 hours before inspection). SIPs panels have pipes pre-installed.
17. Electrical Rough-in (in addition, rough-in extras like alarm systems or wall vacuums). SIPs panels conduits are pre-installed.
18. HVAC Rough-in.
19. Plumbing and Electrical Rough-in Inspection
20. Have Permanent Electricity Hooked Up (Not all electric companies will do it this early but it's great if they will).
21. ~~Install Wall Insulation.~~ Completed at SIPs Factory.
22. Start Exterior Siding
23. Install Sheetrock (1/2 inch is fine)
24. Finish Sheetrock
25. Order Cabinets and Trim
26. Primer on Sheetrock – I know contractors who don't believe in priming sheetrock saying 2 coats of paint are sufficient. Priming is the most important thing you can do for painting. You can put 5 coats on an unprimed wall and it will still leave shadows. I first discovered this fact when I was repainting the first house I ever lived in. Coat after coat was just sucked right into the walls. Also use tinted primer.
27. Two Coats of Paint – If you decide on real deep colors (like Candy Apple Red) be prepared for several coats.

28. Hang Interior Doors and Trim (Cabinets, Vanities etc.)
29. Paint Two Coats on Interior Trim (prime first if not pre-primed).
30. Should Be About to Complete Exterior Siding, Brick Etc.
31. Do Exterior Trim – Soffit, Metal, Gutters and Shutters etc.
32. ~~You Can Place Blow-in Attic Insulation Any Time after This. (Should be at least R-48)~~. Sips roofing panels are insulated at the factory
33. Place All Exterior Concrete (walkways, driveways and porches etc.)
34. Seed and Straw Yard and Install Landscaping
35. Build Decks
36. Install floors in kitchen and baths.
37. Deliver lighting, plumbing fixtures and appliances.
38. Finish Electrical Work – Lights, appliances etc.

Finish Electrical Work – Hanging lights, receptacle covers etc.

39. Do Final HVAC – Setting Units, installing grills & filters etc.
40. Final Inspections Electrical and HVAC
41. Set Plumbing Fixtures
42. Final Plumbing Inspection
43. Do Interior Punch List
44. Install Wood Floors (Some builders try to do flooring earlier. Don't let them because some dumbass will come through the house with mud on his feet and gravel stuck in the mud ruining your floor.)
45. Install Carpets (Be sure the contractor cleans the floor very well before carpet is laid. My carpet guy

says he sometimes has to sweep up trash, mud and other crap before he can start. If you put carpet on a filthy floor it will always be filthy.

46. Final Cleanup
47. Exterior Punch list
48. Final Inspection If Required.
49. You're Ready to Move In.

Modular Housing

Modular housing has gotten a bad rap by some because the industry as a whole has done a terrible job at informing the public. Many people still think that a modular home is a mobile home; however the only thing they have in common is they are both built in a factory and then delivered to the site. In the early days modulars were cheaply built, those days are long gone. Mobile homes are built on 2 or 3 steel rails with wheels and the tires are attached to the rails for transportation. The wheels can be removed, the rails cannot. You can set it on a block foundation but the floors are still supported by rails. The size is limited to 24 feet wide because you can only transport a maximum of 12 foot widths on U.S. highways. In addition, mobile homes are usually built with 2"x 3" studs in the walls with little insulation in the walls or ceiling. They normally have cheap metal roofs and cheap materials throughout the construction.

On the other hand, a modular home is built in a large factory using the exact same process as used in a stick built home. It is delivered as boxes and assembled on site. The floors are either supported with floor trusses or 2x12's, 12-

16 inches on center. The walls are framed with 2x4's or 2x6's and the roofs are framed with trusses. They have either 3 Tab or dimensional shingles just like a site built home. These homes are built entirely indoors so nothing gets wet or is ever exposed to the weather until they are set on site.

These homes are manufactured in sections called boxes or modules. Sections are still limited to 12 feet wide because of the highway limitations, yet the number of boxes strung together is almost unlimited. The company I have used for years has a standard plan that is 7,800 square feet. They have built hotels, large apartment complexes, and several college dormitory complexes.

The foundation for a modular home is built exactly like a foundation for any other home with one exception. Because of the 12 foot limitation, open spans in the basement are limited to no more than 12 feet; meaning there must be a wall or support beam every 12 feet in the basement or crawl space. Given that every foundation requirement is the same as a site built home. Nothing more or less is required.

The volume of work to be done by each trade is either eliminated or greatly reduced as most all of the work is done in the factory. The electrician is only needed to hook up the breaker box and complete whatever minor hookup to the local power system not done by the power company. The plumber only needs to make the connections to the septic or sewer system. The HVAC sub-contractor needs only to do the low voltage hookups and set the units. All the insulation is done at the factory except for the blow-in attic insulation.

The only time you need a framing crew is on set day where they are needed to help set the boxes in place and about a week later to build porches and decks if applicable. The roofer is needed for about a day to lace in the shingles where the boxes come together and the sheetrock guys are only needed to touch up minor transportation cracks. Depending on the plan, I will normally have two people work for two to four weeks after the house is set, mostly to do touch up painting, build porches and decks, finish out siding and do miscellaneous jobs that need to be done after transport. I normally have the flooring done completely by a local flooring company. Yet all the flooring can be ordered with the house package.

As with the last three systems, I am going to skip the early steps for the checklist (1-35) to the completion of the foundation. (See traditional stick framing at the beginning of the chapter)

1. Send your plan to the modular manufacturer so they can redraw the design to accommodate the modular system. Many companies can design your home from scratch. Be prepared to put down a deposit for the drawings (around $2,000). That is normally credited back on delivery.
2. The modular manufacturer will modify your drawings and send them to the appropriate

state agency where they will be stamped when approved.

3. Take the stamped drawings to the local building inspector at least one week before you are ready to break ground. They know they have little input into the main house design but again showing them the proper respect is always a good start.
4. You will pull your local permits, excavate and complete the foundation while the home is being constructed.
5. Set any beams and build any required walls in the basement or pour piers and set beams in a crawl space. Foundation needs to be complete on set day.
6. The set day will be a date agreed upon by the manufacturer and your builder. A crane is needed (rated for at least 75 tons) on site when the home arrives. Depending on the manufacturer you choose, this will be provided by either the company or your builder. In our area, a crane this size costs about $275 per hour including drive times. I have always paid this and lined up the crane on the projects I have done. It averages about $2,000 per home but will be higher on larger homes.
7. Most manufactures do not finance these homes so expect to have a certified check on site on delivery (set) day.
8. Your builder will need 5-6 people on site to assist in setting the boxes on the foundation

and preparing the boxes to be unloaded and set.

9. When all the boxes are set your builders framing crew will work to tie the boxes together at the foundation and roof lines. We tarp over the joints where the roof lines meet and have the roofer lined up the next day to lace in all the joints with shingles provided.
10. On day three after the roofers are finished, I have two or three carpenters ready to finish up the last details from the set. The boxes are bolted together at the floor joist or trusses. The roof trusses for each section are tied together with collar beams and bolts, and the last shipping straps are removed.
11. On day four we usually start whatever siding work needs to be completed. On a home with Hardie Planks or vinyl siding, the carpenters complete one side while the brick or stone masons start on the other (if applicable). It will take between one and three weeks to complete the entire "button up" of the exterior.
12. While the carpenters and masons "button up" (industry jargon for finish up) the exterior, the sheetrock crew will repair any nail pops and transportation cracks in the sheetrock. The plumbers and the electricians make their final connections, and if they won't be in the way the HVAC units can be set and connected.

13. When all the siding work is done then the porches, decks, and patios are built.
14. When the porches and patios are complete, the driveway and sidewalks are poured.
15. After the exterior concrete is in place, the yard and landscaping are planted.
16. A couple of days after the sheetrock guys finish, the touch up painting is completed by either a painter, or in my case, my carpenters.
17. We then do a final cleanup.
18. The flooring is installed and vacuumed.
19. You're ready to move in.

Now that we have completed the checklists you should have a pretty good idea of the general process. Now I'm going to give you a few formulas you can use to determine if you are correct, in case you feel like you are getting nailed somewhere.

Formulas Used in Home Construction

Material estimating for homebuilding is pretty straight forward and simple. I am including this section only so you will have an idea how it is done. If it does not interest you just skip it, but it is good to know it is here if you ever feel the need for the information.

Number of 8" or 12" Block in a Wall – linear feet of wall x height/100 x 112.5

Example: Let's say you have a wall that is 40 feet long and 8 feet tall. 40'x8'=320 sq. feet- 320 sq. ft. /100 sq. ft. = 3.2 x 112.5 = 360. (Add 5% for waste = 378 block)

Bags of Mortar for 8" and 12" Block – I figure 4 bags (80 lb.) per 100 – 8" block and 3 bags per 100 – 12" block. So for 360 block it's: 360/100 = 3.6 x 4 = 14 ½ or 15 bags for 12" block. It is: 3.6 x 3 = 11 bags (includes waste factor). Sand is about 1 ton of sand per 250 blocks.

Concrete Fill for 8" Block– One cubic yard of concrete will fill 80 – 8"x 8"x 16" block. So for 360 blocks the calculation is: 360/80 = 4.5 cubic yards of concrete fill. This is commonly called pump mix.

Concrete Fill for 12" Block – One cubic yard of concrete will fill about 50 – 12"x 8" x 16" block. So for 360 - 12" block the calculation is: 360/50 = 7.2 cubic yards of concrete fill.

Brick and Stone Masonry Formulas

The official number for estimating brick is 6.75 brick per square feet. Most builders' use 7 brick per square foot. In the real world you are going to figure it per 100 square feet. (This is for standard brick 8"x4"x2 ¼").

Example: Let's say we are building a retaining wall 40 feet long and 4 feet tall using 8" block with the front covered with brick and the top covered with brick.

Calculation = 40' x 4' = 160 sq. ft. plus 40'/2.25" for top brick. 160 x 7 = 1120 brick + 10% (for waste) =1232 brick. Add in the brick for top: 40x12= 480"/2.25" = 214 brick. The 10% waste factor above will cover waste of top brick.

Mortar = 7 bags (80 lb.) per 1000 brick. So figure 11 bags for this job, maybe 12. Sand will run about 1 ton of sand per 1,000 brick.

Mortar for stone varies with size. See the stone manufacturer's recommendation.

Gravel

Most residential concrete flatwork (driveways, sidewalks, etc.) calls for 4 inches of gravel for the base. I always figure 5 inches because the ground is going to vary a little.

Example: A typical driveway in a subdivision will be 50 feet long and 20 feet wide. So to calculate the volume of gravel needed 50'x20'x.42' = 420 cubic feet/27(because 27 cubic feet makes a cubic yard) = 16 cubic yards (rounded up). A cubic yard of dry loose gravel weighs roughly 2,800 lbs. and there are 2,000 lbs. in a ton. So 16 x 2,800 = 44,800/2000 = 22.4 tons or 25 tons, which is about one truck load. One cubic foot = Length x width x height (depth).

To use gravel as backfill against a foundation or a retaining wall, bury a minimum of 4 inch perforated sock pipe with 2 feet of #57 stone and cover the width of the base of the ditch.

Example: For a 40 foot wall you will need 50' of sock pipe and 40'L x 2'W x 2'D = 160 cubic ft. of gravel.160/27= 6 cubic yards. 6 cubic yards x 2,800 = 16,800 lbs. Then 16,800/2,000 = 8.4 tons, or call it 9 tons.

Concrete Work

Volume for concrete is calculated much like gravel. Volume = Length x Width x Depth. Example: In the driveway example we will again use 5 inches as our depth to cover ground variation and waste, 50' x 20' x .42' = 420 cubic feet. Concrete is delivered by cubic yards so 420 cubic feet/27 cubic feet per yard = 15.55 or 16 cubic yards. You don't want to waste material; however if you figure a concrete job too close you will have to order a partial load. Anything less than 5 cubic yards will incur a hefty delivery charge, so cut your builder a little slack if there is a little concrete (1/2 yard or less) left on the truck when the pour is finished.

Framing Materials

We now have a pretty good idea of the quantities of materials required to get us to a finished basement. Now we should talk a little about lumber. I will only discuss traditional framing and O.E.V. because the other methods are systems where the manufacturer is giving you a complete price. Keep in mind, with the systems your builder will have to purchase a few pieces of lumber here and there, but that should not add up to more than a few hundred dollars.

Traditional or Stick Framing

To keep things simple, any time I have talked about stick framing or any type of wood framing, I have used floor trusses and roof trusses. While that is not purely stick framing, calculating dimensional lumber for floors and roofs has so many variables dictated by design, it would be impossible to be accurate. Besides I never recommend stick framing floors and roofs because the money you save on material is quickly eaten away by extra labor, plus you get an inferior product.

For our purposes I will stick to calculating material for walls, stairways and floors. First the method for calculating wall materials, framed in wood, is dependent on the framing method you choose.

In traditional stick framing, walls are built with precut wall studs spaced 16" on center with a bottom plate and two top plates. Extra material is needed for windows doors and corners. Precut studs are commonly offered in lengths of 92 5/8" for 8 foot walls, 104 5/8" for nine foot walls and 116 5/8" for 10 foot walls. This makes it possible to have finished ceiling heights of exactly 8 feet, 9 feet or 10 feet without having to cut each stud.

For studs spaced at 16 inches on center (o.c.) you would calculate one stud per linear feet of wall plus 10%. You figure one per foot instead of every 16" plus 10% in order to account for the extra material needed for windows, doors, and corners. This is the way I order studs and it works pretty good, certainly well enough for our purposes here. In addition to studs, a traditionally built wall will require a single bottom plate and two top plates. 2x4x16' or 2x6x16' pieces are routinely used for these.

So let's say we are building a single story home with 250 linear feet of walls. This is what we would need: 250' x 1 stud per foot = 250 wall studs + 10% = 275 studs. 2x4 or 2x6 top and bottom plates are 250/16 = 16 pieces x 2 and I usually add 2, so 34 pieces total. In addition we need 7/16 OSB (oriented strand board) or plywood sheathing to tie it all together. If we had 9 foot walls I would order 250 linear feet x 9 feet = 2250 square feet. Since OSB (I use) comes in 2'x4' sheets, you would have to make up the extra foot in height. 2250/32 sq. ft. per board = 70 sheets + 10% = 77 sheets. I ordinarily order one 50 lb. box of 16 penny hand drive nails and 10 lbs. of 8 penny hand drives. I let the framers provide their own nails for their nail guns because they have about 4 or 5 different options depending on their gun.

For stairs let's just figure a typical 8 foot basement. First you will need three 2"x12"x12' pieces for stringers. I would normally use non-treated southern yellow pine for stringers and use a piece of leftover treated material under the bottom step to keep the non-treated off the concrete floor. With an 8 foot tall basement, you have a rise at a total of 96 inches. 7 ½" is the perfect step height for risers so you would have a total of 12 treads plus the step onto the first floor. At a tread width of 3 feet that works out perfectly using 12 foot 2x12's so you would need 3 pieces for the treads.

Calculating the Advantech® sub-flooring could not be much simpler, square feet of floor divided by 32 square feet per sheet.

Example: 2,200 square feet of floor space /32 = 69 pieces and since there is very little waste, make it 70.

Figuring roof decking and shingles is awfully complicated and really beyond the scope of this book. If you are not familiar with slope or trigonometry it would probably just confuse you. Any roof other than the most simple can get complicated in a hurry so I would leave that to your builder.

Keeping your own records

While you may not be managing the project on a daily basis, keeping your own records is important. A copy of the contract, as well as every piece of correspondence, bills, statements, and a record of any discussion with the builder needs to be filed in a way that you can easily find them. Emails should be printed out and filed. Your builder needs to be aware you are keeping records.

Typical Draw Schedule for Lump Sum Contract (builder pays the bills and is reimbursed)

1. **First Draw (Slab and Foundation) 15% -** This draw includes everything necessary to get to a completed foundation including, but not limited to, permits , site work, soft costs like insurance etc., materials, labor, rough-in plumbing, and land, if applicable.
2. **Second Draw (Framing and Rough Carpentry) 10% -** This draw occurs after the foundation is complete and the framing is complete except for roofing. It includes windows and exterior doors installed, materials, labor, and any soft costs incurred.
3. **Third Draw (Roof and Mechanical Rough-ins) 20%–** This draw will include roof trusses, roofing, plumbing, electrical and HVAC rough-ins. It may also include things like detached garages and progress payments for partially complete brick and siding.
4. **Fourth Draw (Interior and Exterior Finishes) 20%** - This draw includes finished and painted drywall, exterior siding and brick etc. completed, and any progress payments incurred.
5. **Fifth Draw (Trim Out) 25% -** This draw includes all interior trim, cabinets, paint completion, flooring, appliances, and the final plumbing and electric.
6. **Final Draw (Project Closeout) –** Final cleanup, landscaping, outside concrete finished up, decks, retainage, and any leftover progress payments. Final draw comes after the certificate of occupancy.

Remember this is just an example. Each contract has its own provisions.

Chapter 6

Making Sure Everyone's Still in Love at the End!

"Gosh, I have to wait five days to buy a gun; but I'm mad now!"

~ Homer Simpson

As I mentioned in the introduction, I decided to write this book out of a desire to make the homebuilding experience the enjoyable process it should be. A family's home is more often than not, the largest investment they will ever make. That being said, emotions run high whenever issues with the home are involved. Up until the near collapse of the financial system in 2008, people born after the 1950s were so used to home values going up, it never really crossed our minds they would ever go down.

Starting in the mid 1990's up until 2006 or so, the average homeowner had come to think of their house as part of their investment portfolio, and as a source of cash through home equity lines of credit. We often discounted our homes traditional role as a place to raise our family in favor of the role of giant piggy bank. I had started my building career in 1998, and other than a short dip in early 2002, we nearly always sold our homes before we completed them. As you can imagine, the shock of 2008 to 2012 caught me off guard as much as it did everyone else. For the first time in my career I could not sell houses at a profit. Even when we managed to sell one, it would not appraise for the value we sold it for. You talk about scary!

As painful as all that has been for me and homeowners worldwide, in the long run I think this may be good for all of us. Hopefully we will return to viewing our homes as what they really are, a place for us to live and raise our families. It should be a place of security and good memories.

Regardless of how you view your home, if you are lucky enough to be able to build and live in your dream home, watching it go up should be nothing short of exciting and a ton of fun. If you will apply some of the lessons in this chapter and in this book, I promise the entire process will be just that -- fun and exciting.

The underlying theme of this entire book is the importance of planning ahead and being realistic about your expectations. The last thing either you or I want is to have what happens to many people happen to you. When the custom home process starts, everyone involved (as I like to say) is kind of in love. The homeowner found a plan they love, purchased from an architect they like, financed by a friendly banker, built by a builder with whom they have rapport, and shared by a spouse, significant other or family they love very much. With such a wonderful start, who would even consider that things could end badly? Yet they do and it happens much too frequently.

The fact you have honored me by purchasing this book means I have an obligation to do everything within my power to help you discover the secrets to keeping this fun. In the end I want to be a loved one too, so here is what I am going to do. Because I'm a builder myself, I have worked with architects, suppliers, sub-contractors, other builders, bankers, lawyers, building inspectors and homeowners from all walks of life. I am going to attempt to show you the process from the prospective of each of these different types of people. Now I don't want to insinuate I have any unique outlook about how others think, but I have had enough experience with these types to have learned a lot about their common concerns and perspectives. With this in mind, following are some of my observations and some stories that hopefully will help to insure everyone will still be in love at the end of your project.

The Architect

Architects tend to be really smart people with a pretty good understanding of the building process. I can honestly say I have liked all of them I have ever dealt with, even the clown who told me he didn't make mistakes. As I mentioned before, the biggest problem in dealing with architects is making sure they don't get carried away, being creative with your money. No part of the process demonstrates that more than in roof design.

Steep roof lines always add beauty and curb appeal to a home; if it is appropriate for the surrounding area. On the wrong lot, especially a small hilly lot that slopes from front to back, a steep roof can actually be detrimental to the look of a home. What you absolutely must be aware of with complicated steep roofs like 10/12, 12/12, 14/12 is cost. Some of these roofs make it very difficult to use roof trusses on them, making it necessary to stick frame, guaranteeing more time with much greater labor and material costs. Many architects would disagree with me on this but nearly all builders would agree completely. A home with a combination of 6/12 for the main roof and 8/12 or 10/12 for gables and small offsets is the best balance of looks and cost. The only time I would go as steep as 12/12 is for a garage with a bonus room above it.

A good service oriented architect can be a real asset to a homeowner. They have a wealth of knowledge about efficient use of space. An experienced architect will understand the building process, make many suggestions on how to save money, deal with your contractor, assist you in tracking costs, and many times help you avoid mistakes. They can also be a great source for finding a competent contractor.

Rapport is just as important here as with the builder you choose. If you are designing from scratch you will be spending a lot of time with this person. To get the most out of an architect try to have an idea what you want on your first visit. It's not as important to know how you want the house designed (that's their job) as it is to be organized in explaining how you live, what you expect and be able to explain what you hope to get out of a home. Is this home for a couple and two small children? Will there be an older parent moving in at some point? Do you see this house being your permanent residence or do you expect to be there only a few years? What kind of budget are you comfortable with? What is more important overall, curb appeal, comfort, environmental (green) concerns? Is your family active outdoor types or do you tend to spend much of your time indoors entertaining guests? I cannot possibly cover every possible scenario, but you get the point.

Make it easy for the architect to make things easy for you. Listen to what they say and consider their perspective, but don't be afraid to disagree with them. Keep in mind you will be the folks living there. Respect their time and be prepared to make decisions. Some people think it's an architect's job to hold their hand and comfort them as they agonize over every minor decision. They want them to take sides and settle arguments. You may find one that will do this; however you are paying out big bucks. If you want to spend it for a wet nurse, you will get much less of what a good architect can provide. Be prepared to pull your load and this professional will be a huge help for you.

Bankers and Mortgage Brokers

I think you probably have the gist of my general opinion of banker types. They are however, by and large, a necessary evil. Most of us do not routinely have a couple hundred thousand dollars lying around to build a house. For the majority we have to finance at least part of our project. The main thing to remember with these guys is they are not doing you a favor. Banks and mortgage companies make big bucks financing homes so keep that in mind. You need to shop long and hard for the best deal. It is amazing to me how varied rates and terms can be from different lenders on the same project. Because we had a couple of refinancing booms over the last decade, folks tend to feel refinancing is a done deal. Historically that's not the case. Your situation, lending standards, and other factors can change without notice.

When you do find a banker you will probably have to pay a variable rate on the construction loan. That isn't a huge deal because rates don't customarily advance much over short periods. Just know for certain that whatever construction loan you choose, it automatically rolls over to a permanent loan at completion. If rates are rising quickly, you may want to reconsider the timing of your project. Now this is my opinion but many people agree. If a permanent mortgage rate is acceptable and you feel you can afford it long term, get a fixed rate loan. Anytime we have turbulence in the housing markets, it's the folks with the variable rate loans that get killed. This is especially true when you build in a period of low rates. If rates are low, you can be assured they will rise sooner or later.

One last thing on bankers, before you sign up for any loan double check with your contractor about his required draw schedule. Early in my custom building career I had trouble getting banks to pay me what I had coming. I always provided them with a detailed estimate and asked for draws at certain milestones in the estimate. No one ever mentioned a problem. At times I would have some moron tell me, "you have billed our customer for $35,000 and according to our criteria you only have $25,000 coming". It would infuriate me because they were given my draw schedule upfront and were given the paid bills with a breakdown showing exactly what comprised the billing. On a couple of jobs we went through the same issue every draw. The poor homeowner was stuck in the middle, between a pissed redneck builder and an idiot banker who could only understand some vague inaccurate checklist. Believe me; you don't want to be in that position.

Lawyers

For the most part, your guess is as good as mine on choosing an attorney. I can tell you it is imperative you hire an attorney with a great deal of experience dealing with contractors and construction law. I've had two attorneys over the years and both have been great. The attorney I use now, I met at a Home Builders Association meeting. He had given several different lectures over the course of a couple of years and it's amazing the horror stories he shared. He stressed the importance of finding an attorney who always attempts to work problems out and only sues as a last resort. He is correct when he says, "In construction lawsuits, as well as most lawsuits, the only winners are the attorneys".

Builders

You are probably going to assume I'm biased on this one and I probably am to a certain extent. My goal in this book is to do my very best to give you tools to make your life easier and happier during your home building project. In that spirit I can tell you, not only is it important to pick the right builder, it's imperative you work to be reasonable and manage your expectations. That's for your benefit, not theirs. Disagreements are most likely going to happen, but they will be minor unless somebody blows it all out of proportion. Remember the principle of K.I.S.S. (keep it simple stupid).

If you have done your initial job, the builder you chose will be looking out for your best interests and will be doing all he can to bring the project in on time and on budget.

Defining a reasonable expectation is always open to interpretation and opinion. I am in no way suggesting you accept shoddy work or inferior products. In fact, the single best way for you to make a difference in the quality of the construction is to follow up on the work as it progresses. However there are ways to follow up and there are ways not to follow up.

After a few years of unnecessary stress and misunderstandings, I finally made a change that at first was very unpopular with my clients. I added to my contract a clause that stated the client agrees to stay off the property during work hours. Most clients balk at this clause when it comes time to sign the contract, yet in the end they always agree it works out great. Since I started with this clause I have only violated it once and that was on the contract that I mentioned on the very first page of this book (fifth paragraph). It was a friend of a friend and they were really adamant they wanted to be able to come and go as they pleased. So I let it happen. It was a disaster, solidifying in my mind the need for that policy.

Nearly every contractor I know prefers <u>not</u> to have clients on site during working hours. Work nearly always slows down; the chances of either the client or a worker being injured increases substantially, and trades people don't appreciate having someone standing over their shoulder. In the case of the client mentioned above, the guy had moved down from North Dakota and didn't understand the difference between building in the south and the frozen tundra he came from. Many of the things he worried about were even wrong for North Dakota, much less in Tennessee. He insisted on being there daily and actually working onsite.

He had moved down early just to "supervise" the construction. I spent more time trying to keep sub-contractors from killing him than I did doing my job. He would constantly claim they were doing something wrong calling me or worse yet their boss, holding up progress and generally pissing everyone off. What really made it bad? He never once had a clue what he was talking about. What a nightmare.

The following section will help you decide if something is wrong or if it's your imagination.

SITE WORK:

Site Grading

- Areas filled in after excavations do tend to settle. Areas at the foundation, ditches and depressions should be filled after settlement so they don't interfere with drainage away from the foundation or away from the property.
- If possible, the final grading and landscaping should be done prior to closing or if not possible before closing, at the earliest date after closing. Hold back money until complete.

Site Drainage

- The necessary grades and swales should have been established by the builder to insure proper drainage away from the home. After final grade, water should not pond or stand in the main areas except in swales for more than about 24 hours and should be out of swales within 48 hours
- The builder is responsible only for initially establishing the proper grades and swales at final grade. The home owner is responsible for maintaining such grades and swales, once they have been properly established.

CONCRETE:

Foundation walls: Shrinkage or cracks are not unusual in concrete foundation walls. Such cracks greater than 1/8 inch in width should be repaired by the builder.

Basement floors: Minor cracks in concrete basement floors are normal. The builder should repair all cracks exceeding 1/4 inch in width by surface patching or other methods as required. Add fiber to all concrete flatwork to reduce cracking.

Vapor Barrier: All basement floors should require a minimum of six (6) mill polyethylene before concrete is poured.

Garage slabs: The builder should repair cracks in garage slabs in excess of 1/4 inch in width by surface patching or other methods as required. I recommend adding fiber to all concrete flatwork (driveways, sidewalks, floors etc.). Fiber makes concrete stronger and reduces surface cracking.

Concrete floors: Except for basement floors or where a floor has been designated for specific drainage purposes, concrete floors in rooms designed for living should not have depressions or areas of unevenness exceeding 1/4 inch in 32 inches. The builder should correct or repair them to meet these specifications.

Concrete floors with finished flooring: Cracks which rupture the finished flooring material should be repaired. The builder should repair any cracks that would adversely affect the performance of finished flooring.

Other concrete work: Concrete surfaces should not have exposed aggregate or depressions greater than 1/4 inch over 36 inches. The builder should be willing to take whatever corrective action necessary to repair or replace defective concrete surfaces. The builder is not responsible for deterioration caused by salt, chemicals, mechanical implements and other factors beyond their control.

Stoops, steps or garage floors: They should not settle, heave or separate in excess of one (1) inch from the house structures assuming "builder installed" soil drainage is maintained by the home owner. Water should drain from outdoor stoops and steps. The possibility of minor water standing on stoops for a short period after rain is normal.

MASONRY:

Basement or Foundation walls: Small cracks not affecting structural stability are not unusual in mortar joints of masonry foundation walls. The builder should repair cracks In excess of 1/8 inch by surface patching or other methods as required. Pits greater than 1/2 inch deep or surface cracks greater than 1/8 inch in poured concrete walls should be repaired by surface patching or other methods as required. Any cracks less than 1/8 inch will be filled by waterproofing materials.

Masonry walls or veneer: Small hairline cracks due to shrinkage are common in mortar joints in masonry construction. The builder should repair cracks in excess of 3/8 inch by surface patching. Builder should not be responsible for color variation between old and new mortar. A small crack in random bricks or stone is natural and does not constitute a defect.

WOOD AND PLASTIC:

Rough Carpentry

- Floor squeaks are often temporary conditions common to new construction. A squeak-proof floor cannot be guaranteed. However, if you've followed my suggestions with the sub-floor installed on floor trusses using Advantech®, glued down and shot with ring shank nails, the floor won't have squeaks.

- Evenness of wood floors: Floors should not have more than 1/4 inch ridge or depression within any 36-inch measurement when measured parallel to the joists. Allowable floor and ceiling joist deflections are governed by the applicable building code. The builder should correct or repair to meet these specifications.
- Bowing of walls: All interior and exterior walls built with wood studs are going to have waves or bowing. Walls should not bow more than 1/4 inch out of line within any 36-inch horizontal or vertical measurement. The builder should correct or repair to meet these specifications.
- Vertical plumb of walls: Walls should not be more than 1/4 inch out of plumb for any 36-inch vertical measurement. The builder should repair to meet this specification.

Interior Finish Carpentry

- Joints in moldings or joint between moldings and adjacent surface should not result in open joints exceeding 1/8 inch in width. The builder should repair defective joints. Caulking is standard. Joints will open when heating is turned on and the builder should be willing to re-caulk joints once, though he would normally not be required to.

Exterior Finish Carpentry

- Joints between exterior trim elements, including siding and masonry, should not result in open joints in excess of 3/8 inch. In all cases the exterior trim, masonry, and siding should never leak. The builder should repair open joints, as defined. Caulking is standard.

THERMAL AND MOISTURE PROTECTION:

Waterproofing

- Leaks where water is actually entering the basement must be repaired. The builder is not responsible for leaks caused by improper landscaping or failure to maintain proper grades.
- The builder must take such action as necessary to correct basement leaks except where the cause is determined to result from home owner action or negligence.

Insulation

- Insulation, air barrier and vapor retarder shall be installed in accordance with applicable energy and building code requirements.
- The builder must install insulation, air barrier, and vapor retarder to meet these standards.

Vents

- The builder must provide attic venting for proper ventilation of the attic space of the structure.

Roofing and Siding

- Roofs or flashing should not leak under normal conditions, except where cause is determined to result from home owner action or negligence or where assembly is damaged by severe weather or a natural disaster.
- The builder must repair any verified roof or flashing leaks not caused by home owner action or negligence.

Metal and Gutters

- Gutters and downspouts should not leak, yet gutters may overflow during heavy rain. I recommend six inch guttering to prevent overflow. The builder should repair leaks. It is a home owner's responsibility to keep gutters and downspouts free of leaves and debris, which could cause overflow.

Sealants

- Joints and cracks in exterior wall surfaces and around openings shall be properly caulked to exclude the entry of water.
- The builder should repair and/or caulk joints or cracks in exterior wall surfaces one time only. Even the best caulking job requires long term maintenance and it's the home owner's responsibility.

DOORS AND WINDOWS:

Wood and Clad Doors – Warping of exterior doors: Exterior doors will warp to some degree due to temperature differential on inside and outside surfaces. However, they should not warp to the extent that they become inoperable or cease to be weather resistant. If you heed my advice and use fiberglass exterior doors that won't be an issue. The builder should correct or replace and refinish defective doors.

- **Warping of interior passage and closet doors:** Interior doors should not warp any more than 1/4 inch measured diagonally and temporary warping should fluctuate with the weather. The builder should replace any door permanently warped more than 1/4 inch.
- Shrinkage of raised panels: Panels will shrink and expand and may expose unpainted surface. Builders are not responsible for this exposure.

Splits in door panels

- Split panels should not allow light to be visible through the door.

- The builder should repair or replace any door where light shines through.

GLASS:

Broken glass - Broken glass not reported to the builder prior to closing is the homeowner's responsibility.

- The manufacturer or builder should replace any broken glass if reported before closing. It's important to not remove any small stickers on the window frames because these stickers provide important manufacturing information about the window.

Garage Doors on Garages

- Garage doors must be installed as recommended by the manufacturer. It's normal for small amounts of water to enter under a garage door during very heavy rains. This can usually be eliminated or reduced by adjusting the downward tension on the closer.

Wood, Vinyl and Metal Windows -Operation of windows: Windows should operate with reasonable ease, as designed. The builder should correct or repair as required.

- Condensation on windows: It's normal for windows to collect some condensation on interior surfaces when extreme temperature differences and high humidity levels are present. Minor window condensation is a result of conditions beyond the builder's control and is not considered a defect. Fogging and condensation inside the windows are a manufacturing defect and should be replaced by the window manufacturer. Some minor air filtration is normal around windows and doors. Poorly fitted weather-stripping should be adjusted or replaced. It may be necessary for the home owner to have storm doors and windows installed to provide solutions in high wind areas. The builder should adjust poorly fitted doors, windows, and poorly fitted weather-stripping.

FINISHES:

Sheet Rock

- Slight "imperfections" such as nail pops, seam lines and cracks not exceeding 1/8 inch in width are common in sheet rock installations and are considered acceptable.
- The builder should repair defects exceeding 1/8 inch in width, one time only.

Ceramic Tile

- Ceramic tile should not crack or become loose.
- The builder should replace cracked tiles and re-secure loose tiles unless the defects were caused by the home owner's action or negligence. Builder is not responsible for discontinued patterns or color variations in ceramic tile.
- Cracks in grouting of ceramic tile joints are commonly due to normal shrinkage conditions.
- The builder should repair grouting, if necessary, one time only. The builder will not be responsible for color variations or discontinued colored grout. Minor cracks in grout lines are unavoidable and should only be a concern if larger than 1/8 inch.

Finished Wood Flooring

- The dumbest thing I've ever seen a builder do is install wood flooring early in the process. Wood flooring should be done just before or just after the carpet. I prefer it to be the very last thing before the final cleanup as long as it's prefinished. Wood floors that are finished after installation should be done before carpet is installed. The builder should repair or replace at his discretion any wood flooring with a gap of 1/8 inch or greater. Using wood filler is standard. The builder is not responsible for scratches caused by moving in or occurring after the final walk thru.

Painting

- The key to a good paint job is proper preparation. Insist that walls be dusted or vacuumed after final sanding and before the first coat of primer. As mentioned earlier; priming of new sheet rock is vitally important. Slight fading of paints and stains are normal in the first year with the severity partially dependent on climate. Proper cleaning and priming will reduce this significantly. If the builder has cleaned and primed properly then he is not responsible for slight fading.

Wall Covering

- Peeling of wall covering should not occur during the warranty period (typically one year).
- The builder should repair or replace defective wall covering applications.
- The builder will not be responsible for discontinued patterns or "bargain basement" wall coverings unless he provided them.

Carpeting

- Carpet seams will show, but any openings are not acceptable. Installer should repair any open seams.
- Wall to wall carpeting, installed as the primary floor covering, when stretched and secured properly should not come up, become loose, or separate from its point of attachment.
- The installer must re-stretch or re-secure carpeting as needed.

Exterior Stucco Wall Surfaces

- Flashing requirements to windows, walls and wall-to-roof connections must be applied per codes
- Cracks are not unusual in exterior stucco wall surfaces. However, builder should repair cracks greater than 1/8 inch in width.

SPECIALTIES:

Louvers and Vents

- Attic and crawl spaces must be ventilated as required by the approved building code.
- The builder must provide for adequate ventilation, but will not be responsible for alterations to the original system. In my opinion, ridge venting and vented soffit provide the best venting in attics.

Fireplaces

- A properly designed and constructed fireplace and chimney will function properly. It is normal that high winds can cause temporary negative draft situations which can also be caused by obstructions such as large branches of trees too close to the chimney.
- The builder should determine the cause of the problem and correct it if the cause is determined to be uncommon.
- **Chimney separation from structure to which it is attached:** Newly built fireplaces will often incur slight amounts of separation. Separation should not exceed 1/2 inch from the main structure in any 10-foot vertical measurement.
- The builder should determine the cause of separation and correct it. Caulking is acceptable.

Countertops and Cabinets

- Countertop lamination: Countertops fabricated with high-pressure laminate coverings should not delaminate.
- The builder should replace delaminated coverings to meet specific criteria. The builder will be responsible for chips and cracks only if noted before closing.
- Gaps between the walls and countertops should not exceed 1/4 inch in width.
- Gaps in seams on solid countertops should not exceed 1/8 inch in width.

Kitchen cabinets

- Slight warping in doors, from temperature variation, is common and should not exceed 1/4 inch as measured from face with door or drawer front in closed position.
- The builder should correct or replace defective doors or drawer fronts.
- Cabinets, ceiling or wall gaps: Gaps between cabinets, ceiling or walls should not exceed 1/4 inch in width.

PLUMBING:

Water Supply System - All on-site service connections to municipal water main or private water supply are the builder's responsibility. Private systems must be designed and installed in accordance with all approved building, plumbing and health codes.

- The builder should repair if failure is the result of defective workmanship or materials. The builder should

only be responsible for connections from the water meter to the house and the interior plumbing system, not problems with supply, unless installed under the supervision of the builder.
- Drain, waste, vent, and water pipes should be adequately protected, as required by applicable code, during normally anticipated cold weather, as defined in accordance with ASHRAE design temperatures to prevent freezing.
- The builder will correct situations not meeting the code. It is the home owners responsibility to drain out otherwise protected lines and exterior faucets exposed to freezing temperatures. In my opinion only freeze proof exterior spigots should used.

Plumbing System - Leaks: No valve or faucet should leak due to defects in workmanship and materials.
- The builder should repair or replace the leaking faucet or valve.
- The manufacturer will repair or replace defective plumbing fixtures, appliances or trim fittings.
- Installation of fixtures, appliances or fittings must comply with their manufacturer's standards.
- The builder should replace any defective fixture or fitting which does not meet acceptable standards, as defined by the manufacturer. The builder is entitled to be paid for re-install if the home owner supplied the fixture or fitting.

Noisy water pipes
- There will be some noise emitting from the water pipe system due to the flow of water. However, the builder should eliminate any "water hammer" which is a loud noise, sounding like a hammer hitting pipes, when the water is shut off.
- Chips and cracks on surfaces of bathtubs, showers, toilets and sinks can occur when the surface is hit with

sharp or heavy objects. If this occurs before closing it is the builder's responsibility to repair or replace the damaged fixture. Damage is typically caused by sub-contractors placing tools or other items in the tubs. To prevent this I will put water in the tub, about 6 inches deep, if there is no risk of freezing.

- The builder should not be responsible for repairs unless damage has been reported to the builder prior to closing.

Septic Tank System

- Septic system shall function adequately during all seasons, under climate conditions normal or reasonably anticipated (based on local records) for the location of the home. Septic system must be designed and installed to comply with applicable requirements.
- The builder must repair or replace, a malfunctioning or non-operating system, if failure is caused by inadequate design, faulty installation or other cause relating to actions of the builder or subcontractors under the builder's control. The builder will not be responsible for system malfunction or damage which is caused by owner negligence, lack of system maintenance or other causes attributable to actions of the home owner or owner's contractors, not under the control of the builder.

Piping - Leaks: No leaks of any kind should exist in any soil, waste, vent or water pipe. Condensation on piping does not constitute leakage, and is not covered.

- The builder must make repairs to eliminate leakage.
- The builder must repair stopped up sewers, fixtures and drains occurring because of defects in workmanship or materials.
- Sewer fixtures and drains must operate properly.
- The builder will not be responsible for sewers, fixtures and drains, which are clogged through the home

owner's negligence or abuse of the system. If a problem occurs, the home owner should consult the builder for a proper course of action. Where defective construction is shown to be the cause, the builder should assume the cost of the repair; where the home owner negligence or abuse is shown to be the cause, the home owner should assume all repair costs.

HEATING and COOLING:

Heating

- The heating system shall be capable of producing an inside temperature of 70 degrees F, as measured in the center of each room at a height of five (5) feet above the floor, under local outdoor winter design conditions as specified in the ASHRAE handbook. Federal, state or local energy codes should supersede this standard where such codes have been locally adopted.
- The builder will correct heating system to provide the required temperatures. However, the homeowner should be responsible for balancing dampers, registers and the other minor adjustments, as well as changing filters to a minimum of every (2) months.

Air Conditioning

- Where air-conditioning is provided, the cooling system should be capable of maintaining a temperature of 78 degrees F, as measured in the center of each room at a height of five (5) feet above the floor, under local outdoor summer design conditions as specified in ASHRAE handbook. Federal, state or local energy codes shall supersede this standard where such codes have been locally adopted.

- The builder must correct cooling system to meet temperature condition, in accordance with specifications.

Condensation Lines

- The builder should provide unobstructed condensation lines at time of occupancy. The builder will correct and adjust so that the blower and water system operate as designed.
- Condensation lines will produce moisture and the builder must provide a way for the condensation to be carried outside of the structure, either directly or with a pump.

VENTILATION:

- Ventilation systems should be installed per code requirements and allow air exchange for the occupants and building are sufficient to control relative humidity and comfort.
- The builder should correct the ventilation system to provide required ventilation rates if not performing to standards. However, the home owner will be responsible for maintenance to fans for ventilation, filter changes and intake and exhaust hoods.

Ductwork

- When metal is heated it expands and when cooled it contracts. The result is a "ticking" or "cracking" sound and is normal. Loud popping, due to stiffening of metal and duct joints commonly called "oil canning" is not normal and should be repaired by the builder.
- The builder should be able to eliminate this sound. Additionally, the builder should re-attach and re-secure all separate or unattached ductwork.

Outlets, Switches, and Fixtures

- Malfunction of electrical outlets, switches or fixtures: All switches fixtures and outlets must operate as intended.
- The builder should repair or replace defective switches, fixtures and outlets.

Ground Fault Interrupt

- Ground fault interrupts (GFI) are sensitive safety devices installed into the electrical system to provide protection against electrical shock. These sensitive devices can be tripped very easily and are designed for kitchens and baths where appliances can come in contact with water.
- The builder must install ground fault interrupts in accordance with the approved electrical code. Frequent, unexplained tripping often means a faulty GFI outlet indicating replacement is required. Builder should replace within the warranty period.

Wiring

- Wiring should be capable of carrying the designed load for normal residential use.
- All wiring must be installed according to all local, state and federal codes.

Now that we have established acceptable standards, we have a baseline we can use to fairly deal with our builder, sub-contractors and suppliers. If the quality meets or exceeds these standards, then you are getting what you're paying for.

If you want this to be a pleasant experience, getting what you are paying for should be your standard. That's what you should demand, no more and no less. I know enough about builders to realize that's what we are all looking for. A customer who will let us know what they expect, have a clue what they should expect, and not expect less than they are entitled to or more than they are entitled.

In other words, a process that is fair and just to everyone involved.

All any sane person really wants in any business deal is to be treated fairly, with respect and to receive what they bargained for in the transaction. Do you want your builder, suppliers and anyone else that is involved in your project to go the extra mile for you? Well this will do it every single time, guaranteed. From day one let your builder and everyone else involved know that you are a straight upright person. You have no confusion about what you want and expect and that you are not looking for something for nothing. You do that and I promise these people will bend over backwards to make you happy. Do not go out of your way to be a horse's ass or be afraid to let everyone know what you want. Be honest, pay as agreed, and try to see the other party's point of view. That's really all there is to it.

You, Your Spouse or Significant Other, Family and Friends

It's a funny thing about people. We can treat the ones we care the most about, worse than people we don't even like.

Building a house can be a stressful undertaking with many ups and downs throughout the process. Many decisions have to be made and those decisions are often emotionally charged. What's important to one family member may seem silly or a waste of money to another. I've been lucky that it hasn't happened to one of my clients, but every day somewhere in the U.S., a couple divorces over events related to building their dream home. Obviously there were other problems involved, yet the homebuilding process is often the catalyst that sends the relationship out of control.

Why does an event with so much potential for hope and happiness often go so wrong? Is it inherently in the process itself or is it in our approach to it? Anytime I have had a project go wrong, I always spent an abundance of time agonizing over what I could have done differently. After many sleepless nights of rehashing an unpleasant outcome, I come to the conclusion that it was entirely my fault and at the same time not my fault at all. How can that be? Surely it can't be both. Well, it is and here's why.

It was entirely my fault because in every instance I had failed to properly educate my customer. I had not cared enough about the client, the process, or myself to insist we did things the way I knew they should be done. Much too often builders, like myself, are so afraid of losing a job, we act in a way that ends up making us wish we had never won it. We try to preserve egos, referee disagreements, repair hurt feelings, and fix things that should never have been broken. After much soul searching, I now realize those things are not part of what people hire me for when building their home. Trying to take on those responsibilities was what kept me from doing my real job. None of these things were ever really part of my job description. However; most builders undertake nearly all these liabilities routinely on every job. In the end, I am responsible for building a quality product on time, on budget, safely and professionally. As the old saying goes; "if you need a friend get a dog". You don't need or want your contractor to be your friend, or perform any of the other duties, at least not while he is building your house.

What you really want your builder to do is worry about what you are paying him to do. I just explained why it was entirely my fault. This is why none of it is my fault. In a word, it's because it is your fault.

Just as the builder has his or her responsibilities, the homeowner has some responsibilities too. Like the builder, your first duty is to take care of your responsibilities. You, as the homeowner, are not responsible to schedule deliveries, oversee sub-contractors, and solve disputes with subs or suppliers. It's not your job to keep the project on schedule or massage the egos of the builder or his employees.

If none of these things are your responsibility, then what is? Well, your job is unfortunately the toughest one of them all. It is your responsibility, in fact your solemn duty, to make everyone else's job simple. It is your job as the homeowner to get out of your builder's way. Yet it is infinitely more important that you preserve the happiness and sanity of yourself, your spouse or significant other, your family and your friends. You are dealing with people in a potentially stressful situation and that is why your job is the toughest of all.

We all know that dealing with people is the hardest part of any major undertaking. In the case of building a home, it can be further complicated by the fact that you need to please the people you love the most. How do you please everyone? You can't, but you can make it easier for the people most important to you to be happy. You can create the atmosphere of compromise where each and every member of the family feels they had a say, and you can keep things calm by being organized and calm yourself.

Lord, Grant Me The Serenity to Accept Things I Cannot Change, The Courage to Change The Things I Can and The Wisdom to Know The Difference.

The Serenity Prayer

The Serenity Prayer is one I say every night. If that offends you, read it again. If you were to add to love and protect those I care about, then you would have a pretty good description of the homeowner's responsibility in the homebuilding process.

When all is said and done, there is nothing more important than maintaining relationships with the folks you are building the house for. After all, you are not building a house; you are building a home, right?

So, how do you do that? Here are a few suggestions:

To Accept Things I Cannot Change – It's happened, get over it. The home building process is rarely so smooth there's nothing to ever get upset about. If something does not go as planned, it is your builder's problem so let him worry about it. Just stay calm and don't worry, be happy. It will all work out!

The Courage to Change the Things I Can – Don't ever be so timid you don't let the people working for you know and understand exactly what you want. Don't be afraid to let your loved ones know what you want and encourage them to do the same. Getting along and being happy does not mean settling. Be sure to get what you want. The trick is knowing what you want, knowing what you have coming, and letting the others in the family get what they want.

The Wisdom to Know the Difference – If you can master this one, then I promise you, the entire process will be a fun and rewarding experience where everyone is still in love at the end.

Things You Cannot Change

- You cannot change any of the codes, local ordinances, stupid fees, or the politics involved in home building.
- You cannot control when a permit will be issued.
- You cannot control the weather or how long the site takes to dry up.
- You cannot control the attitude of sub-contractors employees or for that matter, the attitude of the sub-contractor.
- You cannot control delays or the pace of work.
- You cannot control hidden hazards. The best you can do is pay attention to any warning signs like rock showing on the surface.
- You cannot control the sequence of the work or how you think it should be done.
- You cannot control delays in key materials.
- You cannot control deliveries that fail to show up on time.
- You cannot control failed inspections.
- You cannot control who the inspector is or his temperament.
- You cannot control every little detail of the work being performed.
- You cannot control the day to day attitude or mood of your contractor.

- You cannot control the situation when a much needed item is delivered broken.
- You cannot control the fact that the contractor has inadvertently hurt your spouse's feelings or generally pissed him or her off.
- You cannot control every person who may wander onto your site.
- You cannot completely prevent an accident.
- You cannot completely stop all worksite theft.
- You cannot control what the new neighbor thinks about your color choices.
- You cannot control the quality of every product or every task installed on your project.
- You cannot prevent every family disagreement over the project any more than you can control any other disagreement.
- You cannot control the situation when a sub-contractor doesn't show up as promised.
- You cannot prevent someone from doing something stupid when they are stupid.

You cannot control the hundreds of things that can and will go wrong on a construction site.

Things You Can Control

- You can have that family meeting to make sure everyone can express their feelings and desires.
- You can spend the time upfront to be sure your plans are complete to the point you don't need additional changes.
- You can set a very realistic budget with a little room (10-20%) for contingencies.

- You can make sure you have the ability to pay for that budget and contingencies. Don't start construction until you are 100% positive you can pay for it.
- You can do enough research to decide on the best type of construction for what you want.
- You can provide the bidders with 8-10 copies of complete and detailed plans.
- You can provide the bidders with a detailed specification sheet.
- You can request a contractor's qualification statement (see chapter 7).
- You can take the advice in chapter 3 of this book.
- You can find 3 qualified contractors.
- You can be sure you and the contractor are properly insured.
- You can make sure to do your due diligence and hire the right contractor.
- You can make sure the winning bidder has all the pertinent information he needs.
- You can make sure that any and all changes are finalized before ground breaking.
- You can stay out of your builder's and his sub-contractors' way.
- You can inspect after working hours, to track if the work meets the standards described earlier in this chapter.
- You can bring any defects to the builder's attention ASAP, but only during working hours. I had a builder friend tell me he once had a client who called him at 2:00 am, saying she couldn't sleep and she wanted to

tell him about a few things. If she had done that to me I would be writing this book from prison.

- You can have enough confidence in your decision to trust your contractor. Remember what Ronnie Reagan said, “Trust but verify”. You can control your emotions and do your best to abide by the Serenity Prayer.
- You can listen intently to well-qualified advice. You still make the final decision but listen.
- You can allow the professionals to do the job you hired them for.
- You can treat this like any other business deal. Know what you want and what you have coming.
- Don’t expect something for nothing.
- Be very clear to your architect and your builder what it is you want and expect. Nothing more nothing less. They will respect you and bend over backwards to help you.
- Tell your contractor everything you think but leave his subs and employees alone.
- Make sure your lender knows the contract’s draw schedule upfront and make sure they can live with it. If they can’t, see if the builder can compromise. If the builder cannot for a legitimate reason, find a new lender. If he’s just being a horse’s ass, find a new builder.
- You can arrange upfront to pay a draw request within 3 days every time.
- If it’s your responsibility to pay subs and suppliers, pay on time.
- Always be realistic and reasonable.
- Demand that your builder is realistic and reasonable.

- Demand that your spouse or significant other and your family are realistic and reasonable.
- If there are any disputes between you and the contractor, your spouse and the contractor, or any other disagreements that become heated, back away and let things cool off. Your chances of winning will be much better and there won't be long term ill feelings.
- Remember that if you did your job upfront, your builder wants to make you happy. He is a human being also. With all the failings that we have, same as you.
- Under no circumstances should you ever let disagreements with your loved ones ever get out of hand. Always use the cooling off period and shut-up until then.
- Always remember why you're doing this and who for.
- Remember Dean Smith's quote on the very first page of this book.
- Always remember, if you follow any of the advice in this book. It will work out in the end.
- Don't forget everything in this book is my opinion. But it is based on tons of tough lessons and years of experience learning things the hard way.
- **I highly recommend you follow the main points of this book.**
    - **DO ALL THE PLANNING AND CHANGES UPFRONT.**
    - **WORK HARD TO FIND THE RIGHT CONTRACTOR AND THE REST IS EASY.**

- **MAKE SURE EVERYONE KNOWS EXACTLY WHAT YOU WANT AND EXPECT.**
- **DON'T EXPECT SOMETHING FOR NOTHING.**
- **STAY CALM, BE REASONABLE, AND ALWAYS REMEMBER TO LOVE AND RESPECT THOSE YOU CARE MOST ABOUT. MAKE ALL THIS ABOUT THE FUN IT SHOULD BE.**

Good Luck, Don't Worry, Be Happy,
The Chubby Builder

If you enjoyed reading this book and you have learned something of value, I hope you will consider giving it a good review on Amazon.com. If not I hope you will contact me with your suggestions to make it better. Please feel free to contact me with any questions or suggestions you may have. Also consider joining my mailing list at:

http://chubbybuilder.com

chubby@chubbybuilder.com

http://amzn.com/B00SF72DH8

Chapter 7

Important Construction Terms

(A)

Abrasive Aggregate – A special type of aggregate or gravel used to make a concrete slab rougher or more abrasive.

Abstract of Title – A deed showing liens and ownership history.

Accelerator – An additive used in a concrete mix designed to speed up setting time and slow down the strengthening process. Most typically used when placing concrete in temperatures under 50 degrees Fahrenheit.

Acceptance – The point where the terms of an agreement are accepted by both parties. Signing the contract follows.

Acceptance Certificate – A formal notice from the builder to the client certifying that the work on a project is complete in accordance with the contract.

Accent Lighting – Lighting fixtures designed or arranged to highlight certain areas.

Action Item – A task to be completed by certain date or time.

Acre – 43,560 square feet.

Accepted Bid – A bid provided by a contractor or supplier that has been agreed to by the client.

Acoustical Board – Construction material designed to block sound between areas.

Acoustical Glass – An interior type of double-paned glass designed to block sound.

Acoustical Tile – Ceiling panels, usually 2'x2', held in place by a hanging metal grid.

Actual Cost – The actual amount spent on a project or phase.

Addenda – Multiple addendums in a contract. (See addendum)

Addendum – An addition, change or correction to the contract documents. An addendum becomes a part of the contract but does not void the original contract.

Advance – An advanced payment (typically 10%) to a contractor specified in the contract and used to pay startup costs of a project. This shouldn't be necessary if you have the right builder. I'll have to admit though, I always appreciated it.

Air-Entrained Concrete – Concrete injected with tiny bubbles to make it easier to work with and more resistant to sub-freezing temperatures.

Airlock – Air trapped in a plumbing system that restricts flow.

Amendment – A change to part of a contract that does not change or void the original contract but only affects the amended part of the contract.

Anchor Bolt – A threaded bolt, nut, and washer set used to tie the sill plate to the foundation.

Angle of Repose – The angle of the excavation that should be built from the bottom of a ditch or foundation over-dig to the top edge of the ditch. This angle prevents the sudden collapse of the ditch's walls and should increase as the depth of the ditch increases. This is very important.

Appurtenance – A clause added to a deed like a right of way or utility setback.

Arch Brick – A type of brick made to build curved shapes like arches.

Arch Brace – A brace built into a roof truss to form an arch.

Arch Corner Bead – A flexible plastic corner bead used to finish sheetrock around an arch.

Architectural – Typically, components like shingles and ornamental components of better than average quality that add to the visual appeal of a structure (see dimensional shingle).

Area Method – A construction estimating method breaking down costs to price per square foot. This is not a very accurate method.

Armor Plate – A metal plate, installed at the bottom of a door, used to protect the door from kicks and scratches.

Aromatic Red Cedar – An aromatic red and white wood typically used to moth proof closets.

Assessment – A property tax that is often attached to specific services by a government agency.

Assignment – A legally binding transfer of rights in a contract. For example, I could assign my rights of payment to a supplier.

Attic – Unfinished space between the ceiling and roof of a structure.

Awning Window – An operating window that is hinged at the top of the sash.

Average Grade –The average of all the elevations within a building site.

(B)

B-Grade Wood – A lessor grade or quality of a surface veneer like plywood or wood flooring that contains visible imperfections and knots.

Backer Rod Foam –Foam used to fill wide gaps before final caulking is applied, and is designed to reduce air flow.

Back Draft Damper –Gravity operated blades designed to restrict air flow to one direction only.

Back charge – A credit to a customer from a contractor or supplier for items or work previously paid on the contract.

Back Vent - A plumbing device installed on the downstream side of a trap to prevent backflow.

Backfill – Soil or other material used to fill over dig around new foundation walls.

Backflow – The flow of water through a pipe in the opposite of the direction intended.

Backflow Preventer – A plumbing device used to prevent backflow in a potable water system.

Backing or Backer Board – A material, in board form, that goes behind or under a finish material to provide added strength or stability. Examples include backer board under ceramic tile and OSB sheathing on walls.

Bad Faith – Intentional attempt to deceive, mislead or cheat in dealings between parties to a contract.

Baffle – Any device intended to change the direction of a fluid, either liquid or air.

Ballast Noise Rating – A measurement of the noise emitted by fluorescent light ballasts. Ratings run from A (quietest) to F (noisiest).

Ballpark Figure – A rough estimate that's really not worth the paper it's written on.

Baluster – A vertical support in a handrail system.

Balustrade – A complete handrail system.

Band Board – A floor joist that runs perpendicular to the other joists and runs the entire perimeter in a wood framed floor system.

Banister – A hand rail system or balustrade running up the side of a stair case.

Base Bid – The amount of money the bidder states in the bid to perform the required work in a contract, before any adjustment or changes.

Base Bid Specifications – The specifications that list or describe those specific materials, products, expectations and construction methods that comprise the base bid.

Base Flashing – Metal strips in roofing that covers gaps between the flat or horizontal roof panels and a vertical section like a wall. It's very important this is done properly.

Base Line – The established reference line in construction and surveying.

Base Molding – Wood or composite trim applied where the sheetrock meets the floor in interior applications, often called base board.

Base Shoe – Quarter round molding that covers up the gap between the finished flooring and the base molding.

Baseline Schedule – The original unchanged schedule.

Batten - A strip of wood placed perpendicular to several parallel pieces of wood to hold them together. The resulting assembly is referred to as board and batten.

Blanket Encumbrance – A lien placed proportionately on every lot in a subdivision.

Bidding Documents – A package of information that includes but not limited to invitation to bid, bid form, specifications, bidding instructions, building plans and any other information necessary to make a complete and accurate bid.

Bidding Period –The period of time beginning when the bid document are distributed and ending at the date and time all bids are due.

Bid Shopping – Sharing pricing information of a bid from one or more builders with other bidders. This is considered unethical and can actually hurt a client's chances for the lowest bid. Don't do it.

BIll of Materials (BOA) – A detailed list of materials and quantities required to complete a project or phase of a project.

Billing Rate – The full value of an hour of labor, including overhead, labor burden and profit.

Birds Mouth – An L shaped cut in a roof rafter designed for a snug fit between the rafter and the walls top plate.

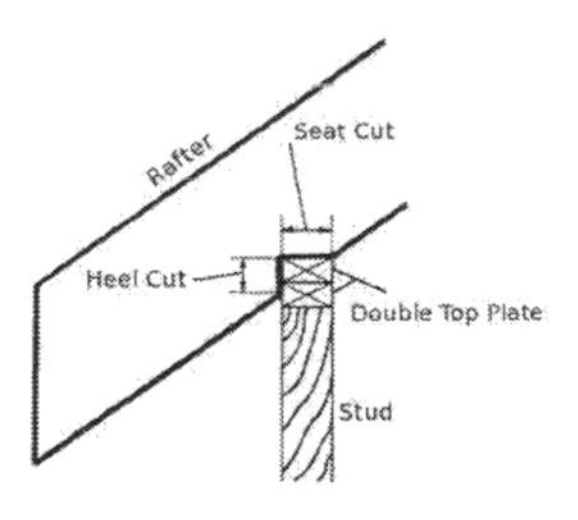

Board Measure – A system for measuring lumber based on board feet. One board foot is a piece of lumber measuring 1 foot long, 1 foot wide, and 1 inch thick.

Bona Fide Bid – A good faith bid that is basically complete and complies with the bidding documents.

Bond – An insurance policy guaranteeing the completion of the contract by the contractor. Called performance bonds or surety bonds, they usually guarantee payment of a contractor's bills. Many homebuilders are not bondable but that doesn't mean they are bad. Bonding qualifications are very stringent.

Boundary Survey – A diagram showing the complete outer boundaries of a lot or piece of property, shows dimensions, angles and compass bearings. Survey must be completed by a licensed surveyor. Don't even consider buying property without one.

Box Stair – An interior staircase built between 2 walls.

Bridge Loan – The financing that "bridges" between an existing loan and an additional loan required to finish a project. If you need one of these, then you haven't been listening.

British thermal unit (Btu) – A measurement used in HVAC systems to measure heating capacity. It is the heat energy required to raise the temperature of one pound of water one degree Fahrenheit.

Budgeted Cost of Work Performed –This is a measurement of the value of work performed rather than the actual cost. Often used by banks to decide draw amounts and can be a source of conflict. Also called earned value.

Budgeted Cost of Work Scheduled – This is a measurement of the value of work that is scheduled to be completed in the future by a certain date. Again, is mostly used by banks.

Builders Risk Insurance – You need to be sure your builder carries this insurance. It's a form of property insurance that covers loss or damage incurred during the construction process.

Burden – Similar to overhead but typically related to labor. It includes all of the costs involved with having employees or subcontractors including workman's compensation, state and federal taxes, vacations etc.

Burn Rate – The rate at which resources like cash or labor hours are either being used or planned to be used.

Buy-In – A bid by a builder that is so low it's purposely designed to lose money, thus pushing out the legitimate bids. The builder hopes to make the job profitable through change orders and extras. Please don't be stupid enough to fall for this bid.

Bylaws – In homebuilding, this would be a set of rules written by a homeowners association governing what can and can't be done in a development. Be sure you understand what is in this document. It's important to know if you can live with the restrictions.

(C)

Cadastral Survey – A large scale land survey done to define the boundaries of lots and other features in a sub-division.

Cadmium Plating – A coating of cadmium over a base metal for corrosion protection.

Caen Stone Cement – A mixture of crushed limestone and cement, finished to look like old stone similar to castles in England and France.

Caisson – A round foundation shaft drilled through loose soil to bedrock several feet below grade. It is built by embedding a vertical tube and filling it with concrete.

Calculated Live Load – The weight that must be considered in beam and joist design to support items that are not part of the structure like furniture, people etc.

Camber - A slight upward curvature built into a beam or truss to offset deflection when loaded with weight. In other words, it will flatten when weight is added.

Camber Window – A window built with a slight arch at the top.

Camel Back Truss – A truss built with the top cord resembling the hump on a camel's back.

Cameo Window – A fixed glass oval window.

Cantilever Footing – Used in the construction of a retaining wall. It's an extra wide footing (3'+) with reinforcing steel turned upward into the block that are filled with concrete. It's very important that any retaining wall over 3 feet tall be built this way to prevent a wall turning over. I always recommend 12 inch block for all but the smallest retaining wall.

Care, Custody and Control – A clause in a liability policy that excludes coverage for the builders work. I got burned by this once when we ran over a septic system with a tele-handler. Liability insurance only covers injuries that may occur on the property during construction. It does not cover screw ups by the contractor. That is why you need builder's risk insurance.

Carpet Density – The number of piles or layers per inch in length in a piece of carpet. The higher the number the better.

Carpet Pitch – The number of yarns across the width of a carpet. Still confused? So am I. You need to let your carpet guy explain this one.

Cash Allowance – An amount set for items required but not specifically described. If the allowance is insufficient, the difference is handled with a change order. A perfect example is one I used to run into a lot. Let's say we have set an allowance for cabinets for $12,000. After going shopping for cabinets the client decides they would rather have cabinets that cost $18,000. The $6,000 difference is then documented in a change order that increases the contract amount. I say I used to run into this a lot because now I do everything I can to be sure they do the shopping up front. It's the contractor's job to keep you on budget but he can't force you.

Casement – A window sash that operates on side hinges and opens and closes like a door but with a hand crank.

Cease and Desist Order – As pertains to building, it's a legal order to stop the building process. It can be issued by a governmental agency or by a client to a builder.

Ceiling Suspension System – A grid of lightweight metal rails and fasteners used to hold a suspended or acoustical ceiling.

Cellular Core Door – A hollow core door filled with honeycomb shaped foam inserts.

Cellulose Fiber Insulation – A wood based chemically treated blow in insulation product. Typically used for blown in attic insulation.

Cement Board – A 3′ x 5′ waterproof board made for underlayment for tile and in wet areas. Durock® is a popular brand name. I recommend you use Hardibacker® board instead.

Center Stringer – One of three stingers in stair system. It is the middle structural 2x12 that supports the treads and risers at the midway point. There are a few builders that will try not to use one on stairs 3 feet wide. Don't fall for it. (Pun intended).

Certificate of Insurance – A form obtained from the builder's insurance agent that serves as a proof of insurance. It shows types of coverage, amount of coverage and the effective dates of coverage. Make sure that you have a copy of workers compensation certificate, general liability certificate and a builder's risk certificate before breaking ground.

Certificate of Occupancy – A certificate issued by the local building authorities after the final inspection that says the construction was built to code and allows the building to be occupied for its intended purpose.

Certificate of Payment – A form issued by an architect certifying that the contractor has completed a task or phase and is entitled to be paid.

Change Documentation Log – A written record of changes and whether they were accepted or rejected by all parties to the contract. It is important to keep this type of log.

Change Order – A written authorization for a change in the contract documents that states all parties agree to a change, the cost of the change, and the details of the change. Never make a change to a fixed contract without one signed.

Change in Sequence – A change in the order of the work planned by a builder. If the change is mandated by the owner then the builder is entitled to compensation. Don't request this unless really necessary.

Chattel – Personal property on premises other than the real estate and buildings.

Chattel Mortgage – A mortgage that is secured with personal property rather than real property.

Chicago Window – A large fixed glass window with narrow windows on each side.

Clean Aggregate – Sand or gravel aggregate that is free of soil, clay or other foreign materials.

Comprehensive General Liability Insurance – A "blanket" insurance policy covering all exposure to liability except those that are specifically excluded.

Concrete Cure and Seal – A liquid chemical treatment that is applied to freshly placed concrete to help retain moisture, to slow curing and sealing the concrete to reduce concrete dust. Highly recommended.

Consequential Damages – Damages that are not incurred by the direct actions of the defendant but are a consequence of another action by the defendant.

Construction Documents – Any and all documents that layout or are related to a construction project. These include but are not limited to contract, drawings, change orders, proof of insurance, construction schedule, draw schedule, construction logs, specification sheets etc.

Construction Draw – Periodic payments to contractors or sub-contractors for work already completed.

Construction Management Contract – My favorite type of building contract. This is a contract where the builder is paid a fee to manage the construction project only and is not required to purchase material or pay labor. The builder may still order the needed materials but must prove what was ordered, delivered and expensed. This is the cheapest way to build as long as the client keeps control over the accounting for materials and services delivered, and is in charge of paying the bills because it removes most of the risk for a builder. A contractor working this way should still carry insurance to protect themselves.

Contingency – An amount or a clause in a contract to cover unforeseen events. Example: A rock clause or money set aside for miscellaneous items.

Contract Dates – Any date specified in the contract documents that affect the contract schedule.

Contract for Deed – An agreement where the seller will deliver title to the property after all required payments have been made. Basically what happens at closing when a builder sells a spec home.

Contractors Qualification Statement – A document presented by the contractor detailing their qualifications, financial position, experience etc. This becomes part of the contract documents. You will have to request this from most contractors. If they provide this without being asked, you should strongly consider hiring them; all other things being equal.

Cost- Plus a Fee Contract (CPF) – A contract where the client pays any and all costs associated with a project and the contractor is paid an agreed upon fee for his services.

Cost- Plus a Fee with a Guaranteed Maximum – Same contract as a (CPF) contract except the clients risk is reduced by the contractor's agreement the project won't exceed a pre-determined amount.

Coupled Window – Two independent window units separated by a mullion strip.

Course – In masonry this is a horizontal layer of brick or block.

Crusher-run Aggregate – Gravel that's been crushed in a crusher and sorted for size. The product includes the powder created in crushing. This is great as an underlayment for paving, concrete driveways and perfect for a gravel driveway because once it gets wet it's as hard as concrete (well, not quite but almost).

(D)

Daily Allocable Overhead – A pre-set amount to be allocated for overhead in the event of extras or delays.

Daily Report Log – A log recording all the activities on a construction site. Typically records weather, conditions around the site, work in progress, accidents etc.

Date of Acceptance – The date the client accepts the work as complete.

Date of Substantial Completion –The date when the project is declared sufficiently complete for its intended purpose.

Dead Load – The calculated weight of a buildings structural components and permanently attached components like framing, roofing electrical systems etc.

Deed Restriction – A restriction on the use of a parcel of real property as laid out in the deed.

Default – Failure to perform a required action in a contract.

Defective – Work or products that are unsatisfactory or do not meet the standards set in the construction documents.

Defective Specs – Mistakes and omissions in the contract documents that impede the work of the builder in some way.

Demand – The electric load required over an amount of time and is typically expressed in watts or kilowatts per hour.

Demand Load – The actual amount of electrical load at any one time.

Demand Mortgage Loan – A type of mortgage that can be called due and payable by the mortgagee at any time. Believe me, you do not want this.

Descriptive Specification – A specification that details very specific requirements of a product, assembly or service.

Design Contingency – An amount set aside for possible design changes during the project. Don't even think about it!

Design/Build – A type of contract where one contractor performs both design and construction services for a client. You should only use this type of contract with a contractor experienced in both fields.

Design to Budget – A clause in a contract between an architect and client stating that a project will be redesigned at no extra charge if the design fails to fall within a predetermined construction budget.

Detailed Construction Estimate – A type of construction estimate using specific quantities and unit prices as opposed to per square foot or ball park estimates. This is the most accurate and what I recommend.

Dimensional Lumber – Lumber cut from 2 inches to 6 inches thick and 2 inches or more wide. Normally starts in 8 foot lengths and progresses in 2 foot increments.

Dimensional Shingles – Shingles cut to a specific size designed to create a specific architectural effect. (See also architectural)

Direct Costs – Any cost directly related to the construction of a building. Direct costs include materials, labor, equipment, fixtures, sub-contractors etc.

Door Schedule – A table in the contract documents listing all doors by size, type, specs and location.

Dormer – A horizontal extension through the slope of a roof extending a room or attic. It has a vertical window at the gabled end.

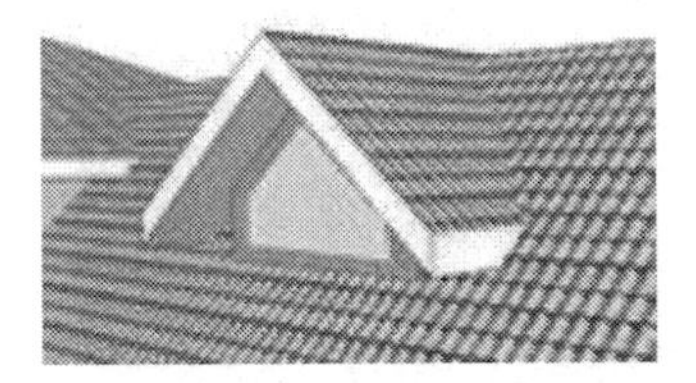

Double Hung Window – A window with two operating sashes. Both sashes move up and down. Modern DH windows typically have sashes that tilt in for easy cleaning also.

Draw Schedule – The pre-arranged schedule of payments from the owner to the builder. These are usually based on a percentage of work completed.

Drought Tolerance – The ability of a plant or grasses to survive drought conditions.

Due Care – A legal term defining the expected standards in the completion of a specific task.

Due on Sale Clause – A clause in a mortgage stating that the entire balance is due and payable upon sale of the property.

(E)

Earnest Money – A deposit made by a buyer of real property showing a serious intent to purchase.

Earth Pressure – The horizontal forces of soil against a wall. Earth pressure is important in retaining walls and basement walls.

Easement – A deeded legal right for limited use of land owned by someone else. Example is a utility easement.

Egress – An exit or way to exit. Windows and doors are good examples.

Elevation – A two dimensional drawing of the interior or exterior of a building drawn on a vertical plane. The best example would be a drawing showing what the front of a building will look like. In surveying it's a vertical reference point.

Elongated Bowl – A toilet built with a few extra inches in front. I wouldn't trade mine for a good horse.

Eminent Domain – The legal right of a government to force the sale of private property supposedly for the greater good. Owner is compensated according to the governments declared value.

Emittance – A percentage of energy absorbed by a solar panel.

Enameled Brick – In masonry it is block, brick or tile with a glazed finish.

Encroachment – Part of a building or other structure built on someone else's property. Best example is when the moron I talked about earlier built the retaining wall and part of the driveway on the lot next door. This includes violating required setbacks or easements. This is very serious and is the main reason you should always use a licensed surveyor.

Encumbrance – A liability or claim against a piece of real property or a restriction of use on a property. Examples include a mortgage, a lien or easement.

Endorsement –An addition to an insurance policy covering a specific loss not covered in the original policy. This becomes a part of the original policy. A good example is an additional insured endorsement in a contractor's policy protecting the client as well as the contractor. It's a good idea for you to have your contractor add you to his policies as an additional insured.

Energized – An electrical line or circuit connected to a power source.

Energy Audit – A survey of heat loss from a structure. TVA has a program called energy right that will rebate part of the cost of appliances and HVAC systems, if they meet certain requirements.

Energy Efficiency Rating – A measure of the ability of an appliance or other product to use energy efficiently.

Engineered Masonry – A brick or block assembly designed and stamped by a licensed engineer to meet specific requirements. A good example would be a retaining wall holding back a large amount of material.

Engineered Wood – Wood products that are made of recycled or scrap wood and are bonded together by a strong adhesive. Oriented Strand Board (OSB) is a good example.

English Bond – Brick work consisting of alternate courses of headers and stretchers or vertical and horizontal laid brick.

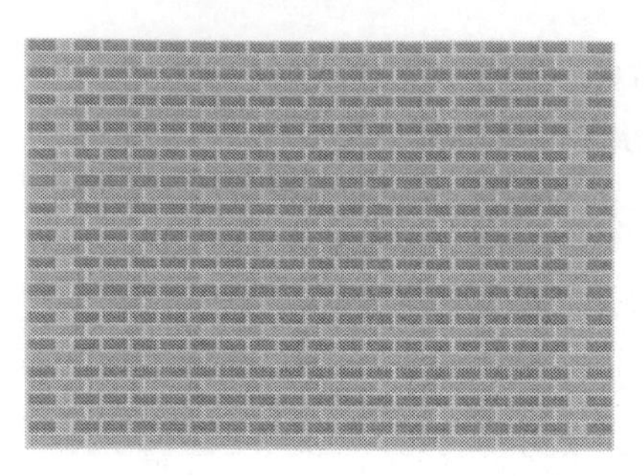

Entitlement – In court proceedings it is a claimant's grounds for a claim.

Envelope – The outside dimensions of a structure.

Environmental Audit – A detailed study of a parcel of land looking for evidence of environmental violations in the parcels history. This is very rarely necessary in residential applications and is extremely expensive.

Environmental Design – Building design that takes the setting or environment into consideration.

Errors and Omissions Insurance – Liability insurance for professionals like architects and engineers covering mistakes and omissions they may make in a design.

Escalation – An increase in either cost or time of a project over and above that stipulated in the original contract.

Escrow – Property, usually money, held by a third party in a special account until a specific action is completed. Earnest money deposits are normally held in an escrow account by a realtor or attorney.

Escutcheon – The protective plate that surrounds a door key hole, an electrical switch or the pipe of a plumbing fixture.

Estimated Maximum Load – The maximum amount of heat transfer that a heat or air conditioning unit might have to provide. EML is used in rating a unit's capacity.

Estimating – The process of determining the anticipated cost of a building project.

Expansion Joint – Used in concrete, masonry or wood construction and is a small gap or cut purposely built in, to allow for the natural expansion of the materials. Expansion joints are very important in concrete flatwork like driveways and slabs to control cracking. All concrete will crack but these joints help to minimize cracking and make it crack where the installer wants it to crack instead of randomly.

Expletive – In masonry it is the stone or other materials used to fill a cavity. In contracting it is the words a builder uses when a client's check bounces.

(F)

Face Block – Block with a finished side for decorative purposes.

Face Brick – Any exposed brick.

Face Line – A reference line a mason sets and follows when building a line, often called a string line.

Factory Primed – Any building product that has the initial undercoat applied in the factory.

Factory Edge – The original, uncut edge of a construction material.

Fast Track Construction – A method of construction where parts of a project start construction while other parts are still in the design phase.

Fatigue – The weakening of a material from repeated loading and unloading of forces. Fatigue can be the cause of cracking or a complete failure.

Federal Home Loan Mortgage Corporation – Nicknamed "Freddie Mac" is a government backed corporation that provides a secondary or resell market for home mortgages.

Federal Housing Administration – Part of the department of Housing and Urban Development (HUD) that provides mortgage insurance for private mortgages, making it safe for banks to make mortgage loans and easier for consumers to qualify for mortgages.

Federal National Mortgage Corporation – Nicknamed "Fannie Mae" is a government backed company that provides a secondary market for FHA and VA loans.

Federal Style – An architectural style first made popular in the U.S. from 1790 to 1840.

Fee Simple – An ongoing and inheritable interest in a parcel of real property giving the owner the right to transfer the property as he or she sees fit.

Fiber Reinforced Concrete - Fiber reinforced concrete is a type of concrete that includes fibrous substances that increase its structural strength and cohesion. I highly recommend using FRC.

Fill Insulation – Any type insulation that is poured or blown into place.

Final Acceptance – The formal, written acceptance of a contractors completed project by the client.

Final Completion – The point where the project is completed according to the terms and conditions in the contract.

Final Inspection – The final walkthrough by a building inspector just prior to issuing the certificate of occupancy.

Final Payment – The last payment on a project where both parties formally agree in writing the contract and any change orders are paid in full.

Final Waiver of Liens – I cannot stress enough the importance of this document. It is the acknowledgement in writing from all suppliers, vendors, sub-contractors and the general contractor stating that each has been paid and they give up all rights to place a lien on the property. This needs to be completed with the final payment.

Finished or Final Grade – The final elevation of the completed construction site. Finished grade includes the top soil, grass, paving, slabs etc.

Fire Brick – A fire resistant ceramic brick used in fire places and chimneys.

Fire Blocking – Horizontally placed pieces of stud material placed between studs to help block the spread of fire vertically.

Fire Wall – An interior or exterior wall running from the foundation to or above the roof line built to block the spread of fire.

Fixed Transom – A fixed glass or panel of glass above a door that is non-operating.

Fixed Price Contract – A type of contract where the contractor agrees to build a project for an exact predetermined price. Can work well for everyone but is a recipe for disaster if the client has not planned properly or is not disciplined about adding anything. This is a more expensive way to build than many other contract methods because the builder must plan and charge for contingencies that may or may not occur. I hate building on a fixed cost contract unless the client agrees in writing not to make changes once construction begins.

Fixed Project Overhead Cost – Direct project overhead costs that are not affected by time or work done.

Fixed Rate Mortgage – A type of mortgage in which the interest rate remains constant for the entire life of the loan.

Fixed Retaining Wall – A retaining wall supported or braced at the top and bottom.

Flash Point – The temperature at which a material or substance will burst into flames.

Flashing – A thin set of material, normally aluminum, placed in an assembly that is designed to prevent water from entering the structure, or to redirect water. Typically is used between a roof and vertical wall section and on hips and valleys in a roofing system.

Flat Paint – A type of paint that dries to a low gloss finish. Flat paint is often used in residential construction to hide imperfections in sheetrock.

Flemish Bond – A brick wall laid in a pattern of alternating header and stretchers in each course. Headers are then centered over stretcher in the next course.

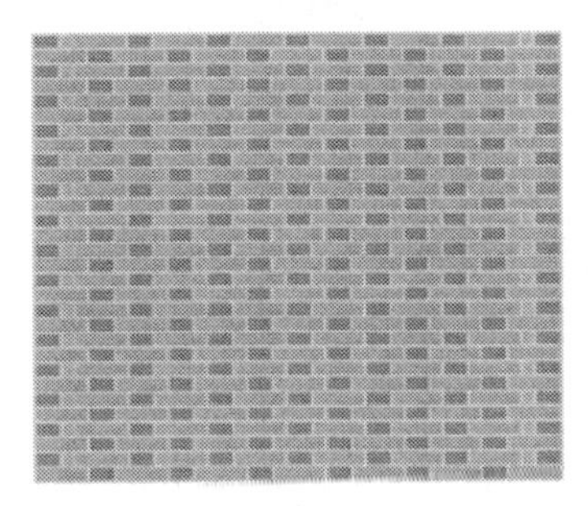

Floating Floor – A floor assembly with an underlayment between the subfloor and the finished floor.

Floor Plan – A flat two dimensional drawing showing the outline of a floor designating the location of interior and exterior walls, windows, doors, room layouts, etc.

Floor System – All of the parts that make up a floor including joists or trusses, sub-floor, finish floor etc.

Floor Truss – An engineered and manufactured replacement for a floor joist. I love using them.

Foam in Place Insulation – A mixture of foam and insulating materials that is sprayed into wall cavities reducing air infiltration better than other types of insulation. I have used it and like it a lot but it can be expensive. You will recover the extra money over time.

Foam Backer Board – A 4 foot x 8 foot sheet of foam insulation used as a backer for siding. FB is available in different R-Values.

Free on Board – A logistics term referring to a point that a shipper will deliver goods for no charge to the buyer.

Frost Heave – When water freezes in soil and causes the soils to rise upward. If a foundation is not deep enough frost heave can create a lot of problems.

Frost Line – The depth that frost penetrates down into the soil. Footers not placed below the frost line may incur frost heave. Frost lines are different in each part of the world. The colder the winter time weather, the deeper the frost line. For example the frost line in most parts of Tennessee is 18 inches or less. In the northern U.S. the frost line can be 48 inches or more.

Full Bond – A brick pattern in which all bricks in all courses are laid as headers. I have included some different bonds so you know they exist. Your brick salesman can show you all the different types.

Furniture Grade – Lumber of a size and quality suitable for making finished furniture.

Furring Strips – Wood or metal pieces used to attach drywall to concrete or masonry walls.

Fuse – A device that protects an electrical circuit from too much current. The device melts inside, shutting down the circuit.

Fuse Box – A metal box with a hinged lid that contains all the fuses for each electrical circuit in the home.

(G)

Gable – An area at the end of a building section, extending from the eve to the ridge of a roof. Typically triangle shaped on a simple ridge roof but shape can vary depending on the roof configuration.

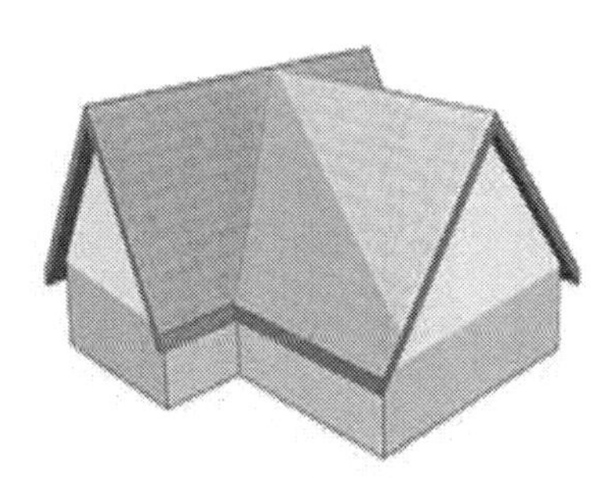

Gable Vents – Vents mounted in the top portion of a gable end designed to ventilate an attic.

Garrison House – A house style where the second floor overhangs the first floor on one or more walls.

General & Administrative Costs (G&A) – Overhead costs like office, phones, trucks and equipment, office staff, etc. These are expenses that all contractors have but are not specifically related to any one job. A contractor charging these costs is not cheating you. These are 100% legit.

General Conditions – The part of the contract where all of the responsibilities, rights and other details of other conditions are spelled out. In the estimate some of the specific G&A costs are itemized.

General Liability Insurance – The insurance policy that protects the overall project and the neighboring properties from non-construction related accidents. Examples would be if someone not working on the property was to fall onsite or a piece of equipment destroyed your neighbor's fence.

General Requirements – Similar to the estimating portion of general conditions. Detail certain overhead conditions like rental equipment, an onsite "Port-a-Potty", etc.

General Terms and Conditions – The section in a contract explaining conditions that apply to all transactions and actions in the contract and not to any specific item. An example might be a clause stating that any changes to the plans must be approved by all parties affected.

Georgia Buggy – Basically a motorized wheel barrow used to move concrete around a site to areas not accessible by the concrete truck. Your builder may have to rent one of these during construction. It is a legitimate charge.

Georgian Style Architecture – A classical style originating in England in the 1700s.

Georgian Window – Another name for a double hung window.

Geothermal Heating – A heating system that circulates water through underground pipes. It uses the heat from the ground to raise water temperatures before adding mechanical heat thus using less energy.

Glass Blocks – Square hollow blocks of glass that diffuse light. Often used in bathroom windows.

Glue Laminated Timber – Called a glue lam in the field. It is timber that is made from layers of wood or laminates, glued together with the grains parallel to each other the long way. They make great beams, columns and headers. I highly recommend using these where appropriate.

Glued Floor System – This is the system I have recommended throughout this book. Use Advantech® sub-flooring glued to floor trusses and fastened with ring shank nails. I used to screw down floors thinking it was great but we found the heads would pop off many of the screws, defeating the purpose.

Grade – The existing or proposed level or elevation of ground.

Grade Line – A string pulled from stake to stake denoting the desired elevation of points along that line.

Gradient – The rate of level or elevation change of a measured surface. For example, if an area of land drops 1 foot in elevation over a span of 4 feet the gradient would be .25 or 25%.

Graduated Payment Mortgage – A mortgage that starts with low payments that go up gradually (often annually) paying off a mortgage quicker than a traditional mortgage.

Grandfather Clause – A clause in a ruling that allows a longstanding practice to remain allowable; when a new rule has been adopted that would not allow that practice in the future.

Grantee (Buyer) – The party in a deed document whom the title or property rights are deeded to.

Grantor (Seller) – The party in a deed document who is transferring title or property rights to the grantee.

Graphite Paint– Used to slow down corrosion on metal surfaces.

Green Building – The use of building methods, materials and practices that lessen the impact on the earth's environment.

Green Concrete – Concrete that has set up but not hardened.

Ground Cover – The use of low, fast spreading plants to cover bare areas especially areas where erosion may be a problem.

Ground Fault Circuit Interrupter – Electrical outlet designed for use in areas where water may be present like bathrooms, kitchens and outdoors. The GFI will kill the power to the circuit if there's a surge, protecting users from electrical shock.

Grounding Rod – A metal rod driven into the ground and attached to the electrical system to serve as the ground for the system.

Groundwater – Stored water under the earth's surface.

Guaranteed Maximum Cost Contract – A cost plus a fee contract where the contractor gets paid for all costs incurred plus a fee that covers his overhead and profit. However, the contractor is responsible for paying any cost over and above this preset guaranteed maximum.

Guarantor – The person or entity that is responsible under a guarantee agreement.

Guy Wire – A cable anchored in the ground at one end and supporting an object like a power pole or wall at the other end.

(H)

Habitable Space – General living areas in a structure. Customarily excludes bathrooms, utility spaces and garages.

Half Round – Molding having one flat side and one round side.

Half Story – A finished attic or other space immediately below a sloping roof. Only part of the floor space has a full height ceiling.

Half-Pitch Roof- A roof with a slope equal to 1/2 the width of the span.

Half-Landing – A platform in a stairway placed half-way between floors where the stairs change direction.

Hardscape – Non-plant landscaping areas like paving, driveways, sidewalks, decorative gravel etc.

Haunched Floor – A concrete slab that is thicker around the outside perimeter. Most often used in a monolithic slab where the footing and the slab are all poured together and at the same time.

Hazard Insurance – Insurance that covers property damage from specific events like fire, storms, wind, etc. This is commonly included in a builders risk policy.

High Performance Building – A building that is optimized for energy efficiency, healthy environment and comfort.

Hip Roof – Hard to explain, see picture below.

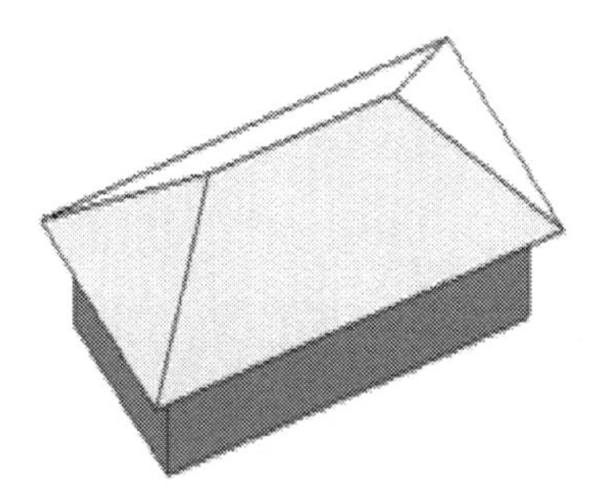

Hip and Valley Roof –A roof with both hips and gables forming valleys.

Homeowners Association (HOA) – A non-profit organization of homeowners in a complex or sub-division that sets rules and manages common areas and common amenities. These things can be very powerful and a homeowner should be sure to understand the local version before buying in a development.

Hurricane Clips – Heavy duty metal anchors used to tie roof rafters or trusses to the walls and floor trusses to other structural members. I have always used these.

Hydro-Seeding – A combination of water, grass seed, fertilizer and binder sprayed under high pressure over a large area. HS is expensive but effective.

Hydrostatic Pressure – Pressure from water or moisture in soils.

(I)

I-Beam – A high strength rolled steel structural beam that has a shape similar to a capital (I).

I-Joist – An engineered wood floor joist that has two flanges connected by a solid web made of OSB. They are sized according to loads and are engineered into the overall structural system. They are shaped similar to a capital (I). They are also referred to as TJIs.

Ice Dam – An accumulation of ice and snow at the eaves or in the valleys of a sloping roof blocking the escape of water.

ID of Long Term Procurements – The process of identifying materials and products that must be ordered early in the process in order to be sure they are on site when needed. Good examples are trusses and cabinets.

Idle Equipment Cost – The cost of equipment that is on site and ready for use but are sitting idle. Ownership or rental costs are ongoing whether they're being used or not. A lot of money can be wasted this way.

Impact Costs – Extra costs that are associated with a change or a delay.

Impact Fees – A charge levied by a governmental agency to offset extra costs related to development like additional roads, schools etc. (mostly BS). Used to slow growth.

Impervious Soil – Heavy grainy soils like clay that blocks the absorption of moisture. These soils make them less suitable for septic systems.

In Place Value – The market value of a product or assembly that includes the price of the material, transportation costs and the cost of installation etc.

Industry Standard – Published and verifiable specifications, codes and other information that is generally accepted by professionals and proven by long-term experience in the construction industry.

Inexcusable Delays – Project delays due to negligence or lack of effort on the contractor's part.

Infrastructure – Improvements to public assets like roads, bridges, schools, utility systems etc.

Inorganic Material – Material like stone that are derived by natural mineral compounding. Not formed from once living materials.

Inspection List – Commonly called a punch list, is a list of uncompleted or defective items that must be corrected before the builder can collect their final payment.

Instructions to Bidders – A formal document that becomes part of the contract documents. An (ITB) provides all the information necessary for a bidder to make a complete bid and indexes all the other documents like specs and drawings.

International Residential Code (IRC) – Published by the International Code Council (ICC). If (IRC) is adopted by local building authorities, it covers the construction of all residential buildings less than or equal to three stories high.

Invitation to Bid – A written notice of an owner's intention to receive bids on a project. Invitation is commonly advertised in local papers.

Invited Bidders – The group of bidders chosen to actually submit a bid.

Iowa Curb – Often called a rollover curb, it is concrete curbing that is a combination of a gutter and a curb that is relatively flat and can be easily driven over.

Irregular Pitched Roof – A type of roof where the pitch will change in the same span.

(J)

J Channel – A plastic or metal channel shaped like a J and used to hold a building material like siding.

Jack Arch – An arch that is almost flat.

Jack Beam –A beam that's used to support another beam or a truss.

Jack Rafter – A short rafter used in hip roofs.

Jack Truss – A truss that is smaller than the other trusses in the system. A jack truss is often used in a hip roof.

Jalousie Window – A louvered window.

Job Order Authorization – A written document signed by the owner authorizing a specific task.

Job Overhead – Indirect costs or job costs other than materials, labor, sub-contractors or equipment.

Job Site – The defined area and boundaries where the project is taking place.

Job Lot – Discontinued products sold at reduced prices. Job lots are similar to closeouts in other industries.

Joint-less Flooring – Any type of flooring that can be installed without joints.

Joists – Structural members set parallel to each other and used to support sub-flooring or ceilings.

Joist Hangers – Metal straps used to support the ends of joists, beams or trusses where a horizontal load bearing surface is not available.

Joist Bridging – Bracing between joists or floor trusses that prevent twisting or rolling over.

Jumbo Brick – Any brick manufactured larger than standard size.

Jut Window – Any window that protrudes or juts from an exterior wall like a bay window.

(K)

K Series – A long span steel joist.

K Truss – Any truss whose web resembles the letter K.

K Value – The ability of any substance or material to conduct heat.

Key Stone – A stone or brick with angled edges that is installed in the top of an arch for decorative purposes.

Keyway – A metal channel imbedded in a concrete slab to provide shear strength and room for expansion. I like to use these in driveways and sidewalks instead of cutting expansion joints. A lot of concrete finishers complain about them because they can be a pain to set.

(L)

Labeled Door – A door with a certified Underwriters Laboratory, Inc. fire rating.

Labeled Window – A window with a certified U/L fire rating.

Labor and Material Payment Bond – A bond purchased from an insurer by the contractor guaranteeing to the owner that all materials and labor connected to the project will be paid.

Labor Burden – Any and all taxes, insurance and other costs associated with payroll that the builder is required to pay.

Labor Hour – The total cost for one hour of labor at the appropriate rate for that particular worker. For example, a labor hour for a carpenter is higher than for a laborer.

Labor Productivity – A measure of work done in relation to labor hours spent.

Labor Rate – The total charge for one hour of labor including profit.

Laborer – A worker with no particular trade skill.

Laminated Glass – A safety glass made with two or more layers of glass and bonded with transparent plastic sheeting. LG is shatter resistant and if it does break, it breaks into tiny pieces.

Lancet Window – A tall, narrow window with an arch.

Land Tie – A heavy anchor; like block, timbers or a cable buried under ground and tied to a retaining wall with a guy wire to prevent the wall from overturning. A land tie is often called a dead man in the field.

Land Tile – A clay vent or a plastic pipe with holes in it covered with gravel and designed to drain water away from an area. More commonly called a drain tile.

Landing – A platform at the top, bottom of a staircase or between two staircases.

Leach Field – The part of the septic system where the liquid waste is discharged and then treated naturally by earth filtering.

Letter Form of Agreement –An agreement in letter form that is mailed or faxed, to be signed and returned by the addressee, and serving as a legally binding document.

LEED (Leadership in Energy and Environmental Design) – The U.S. Green Building Council's rating system used to evaluate a buildings environmental performance.

Let or Sublet – Issuing a contract for a smaller portion of the project.

Letter of Intent –A notice expressing the intent to enter into a formal contract.

Leverage –The relationship between debt and equity in real estate.

Lien – A legal notice of an unsatisfied debt or obligation tied to a piece of real estate. This notice is filed with the local registrar of deeds and will prevent the transfer of the real estate until the lien is satisfied.

Lien Waiver – A document signed by a party with the possible right to file a lien on a property. The lien waiver says that the party signing it gives up any right to file a lien on that property. Lien waivers are either partial or full. You need to have a partial lien waiver signed by any and all parties supplying labor or material each time a payment is made and more goods or services will be provided later. Once the vender is 100% finished and paid, they will need to sign a final lien waiver.

Limit of Liability – The maximum amount of money an insurance company will pay for a covered loss.

Live Load – The load on the structural members of a building related to the use of the building. LL includes furniture, fixtures, people etc., it does not include the building components themselves (described as dead load).

Load – Load is the force or forces that are acting upon a structural system or individual part. A good example would be the weight being supported by a beam.

Load Bearing Wall – A wall that is designed, built and placed to support a load in addition to its own weight.

Loan to Value Ratio – The amount a lender is willing to loan on the appraised value of real estate.

Locus – A small street map included on the house plan to show the basic location of the site.

Loose Estimate – An estimate that allows for extras and the unexpected. The LE is sometimes called a safe or high estimate.

Low Impact Development – A building project that minimizes its effect on the surrounding environment.

Low VOC – Any building material that has a low release of volatile organic compounds or gasses that can affect health and comfort. Low VOC is an important factor in the green building movement.

Lowest Responsible Bidder – The lowest bidder who is actually capable of completing the project. In the example I gave of my friend's experience where the client took a ridiculously low bid, the winning bidder was the low bidder but not the lowest responsible bidder. Don't make the same mistake as that clown.

Lump Sum Agreement – Another name for a fixed sum contract.

(M)

Made Ground – Areas made or created by filling in low places with loose fill materials other than compacted gravel. Made ground cannot be built on unless building uses caissons or pilings.

Mahogany – A medium density wood that is mainly used in cabinets and furniture.

Main Divisions – Refers to the division of labor between the prime contractor and the sub-contractors.

Maintenance Bond – A bond issued by an insurer that guarantees to the owner that the builder will repair any defects in materials or workmanship for a specified period. It is typically part of a performance bond and is void after 1-2 years.

Man-Hour – The measurement of one hour of work for one person.

Manifest – A list of all items contained in a shipment.

Mandate – A court ordered directive that must be obeyed under penalty of law.

Mansard Roof – A roof with a multiple pitch on all four sides with the lower pitches being very steep.

Manufactured Home – Any home where the majority of the assembly is done in a factory.

Manufactured Wood – See the definition for engineered wood. Also includes trusses, laminated beams etc.

Manufacturers Specifications – Detailed installation instructions sent with many building products. Failure to follow these instructions can void any warranty provided.

We once ran into this when we went to replace a friend's roof in my neighborhood; built by another builder that had failed after about 5 years. When we contacted the manufacturer to honor the warranty, they sent out a representative who showed why the warranty was being voided. It turned out the shingles had been "high nailed" which means the roofing nails had been installed much too high on the shingle, missing the spot where the shingle pieces came together causing the shingles to slide down the slope.

Margin – The amount of money a contractor will add to materials or labor over and above the cost of the M/L.

Market Approach – An appraisal method that values a home or property by comparing it to recently sold similar properties.

Market Value – The price based on the amount required to attract a qualified buyer given the current conditions in the local housing market.

Marketable Title – A title that has no defects.

Master Builder – A certification by the National Association of Homebuilders (NAHB) certifying that a contractor has completed and passed about 30, four hour classes. I have taken several of these classes. I can tell you, it is a big deal to have taken all of them.

Master Schedule – The original detailed construction schedule that includes all the specifics of the project and organizes the critical path tasks that must be completed before other tasks can begin.

Mat Foundation – A thickened-slab foundation designed to support an entire building. MFs are most often used when a buildings weight needs to be spread over a wide area like over unstable soils.

Material Safety Data Sheets (MSDS) – A government mandated form provided by hazardous material manufacturers explaining all the facts, safety information and treatment recommendations for their products.

Means of Egress – Any permanent exit from the inside of a building directly to the outside.

Mechanical Plan – A separate page or pages showing the layout for plumbing and HVAC systems.

Mechanics Lien – A lien on real property for non-payment of invoices relating to building services or material.

Mediation – A method of dispute settlement where an impartial third party is employed to suggest ways to settle the dispute. Mediation can be binding or non-binding.

Metes and Bounds – The outer boundaries of a property as calculated in a survey.

Metric Ton – A weight equal to 1,000 kilograms or 2,205 lbs.

Mezzanine – A suspended floor between a lower floor and a ceiling that's smaller in area than the floor below it. Think of it as an interior balcony.

Micro-lam –Refers to laminated high strength structural engineered wood beams. These are high quality products that I recommend.

Mildewcide- A chemical used to slow down or stop the growth of mildew. Top quality roofing normally includes this treatment.

Minimum Acceptable Pressure – The minimum water pressure required for a water system to operate properly.

Mission Tile – A type of clay roofing tile that resembles cross sections of cylinders cut in half and used on a sloped roof with the concave side alternating between up and down.

Mitigation of Damages – A legal duty by an injured party to attempt to keep damages from getting worse. For example if a water pipe broke and was flooding the basement, it would be the owner's duty to try to turn the water off if he knew about it.

Model Codes – Widely accepted, professionally prepared building rules and regulations designed to bring uniform protections to occupants of buildings. The International Residential Code is a good example.

Modular Construction or Modular Housing – The construction method where large sections or modules of a building are manufactured 85-90% complete offsite, transported to the site and then combined to build a complete house. Modern day modular housing, built by quality companies, is a viable and efficient product.

Moler Brick – A type of brick with better insulation value than standard brick.

Mono-Slope Roof – A roof with a constant slope in one direction. A shed roof is a good example.

Moratorium – A temporary halt to all development by a building authority.

Mortgage Origination Fee – The charge for preparing and servicing a mortgage application.

Mortgagee – The mortgage lender.

Mortgagor – The borrower in a mortgage transaction.

Mud-jacking – A method of raising unleveled concrete slabs by drilling holes into the low side and pumping the underside of the lab full of a thin set concrete mix.

Mullion Strip – The vertical metal or vinyl strips that separate the panels or lights in a window or door.

Multiple Listing Service – A database operated by the local realtors association listing information about properties for sale or lease in the local area.

(N)

Negative Easement – The right of one landowner to prevent his neighbor from doing something on the neighbors own land. For example, if neighbor one has a negative easement for an unobstructed view of a mountain range, he may be able to prevent neighbor two from building a two story house.

Negative Float – The number of days that an important task is behind schedule.

Neoprene Waterproofing – Neoprene sheeting placed on the outside of basement walls for waterproofing. (Good Stuff)

Net Floor Area – The livable areas of a home not including wall thicknesses, hallways, stairways and attics.

No Damages for Delay Clause – A contract clause stating that in case of a delay the contractor will receive a time extension but not any monetary compensation, no matter the cause.

Noise Insulation – Sound absorbing material installed in interior walls to reduce noise transmission from one room to another.

Nominal Dimension – In wood and many other building products true dimensions are actually smaller than nominal sizes. For example a 2" x 4" stud's nominal size is 2x4. Its true dimensions are 1 1/2" x 3 1/2". The difference is due to shrinkage due to kiln drying.

Non-Bearing Wall – A wall designed to not carry any load other than its own weight.

Non-Cohesive Soil – Soils in which the particles don't stick together, like sand and gravel.

Non-Collusion Affidavit - A written statement by a bidder, swearing there were no secret agreements or side deals made in order to obtain a contract by fraudulent means.

Non-Conforming Work – Work that does not conform to the requirements in the contract documents in some way.

Non-Excusable Delay – A delay in the project that was solely the fault of the contractor on which he will receive neither a time extension nor monetary compensation.

Non-Combustible – A material that won't ignite or burn when exposed to fire.

Non-Combustible Construction – A construction method in which all the walls and structural materials are built from non-combustible materials. A building with metal framing is a good example.

Non-Pressure Pipe –A pipe with no pressure rating so it can only be used for venting or gravity fed waste pipes.

Non-Restrictive Specification – A specification with no restriction on brand or supplier.

Notice to Proceed – A written authorization from the owner or a building authority to the builder allowing work to begin on a project.

Novation – An agreement from one party to release another party from a contract in exchange for allowing a third party replacement.

(O)

Obscure Glass – Glass that allows light through but does not allow a clear view of objects on the other side.

Glass block with obscure glass is often used for bathroom windows.

Occupancy –Using a building for its intended purpose.

Occurrence – For our purposes, occurrence is an insurance term meaning an incident or event. A wind storm knocking down your roof rafters is an occurrence. An occurrence is different from an accident.

Offer and Acceptance – When a contract has been agreed on and signed.

Offset – The scale used on a plan. Scale for a house plan is normally 1/4"= 1 foot.

Offset Stakes – Stakes set in line with but past the corners of a building. These L shaped frames are used to tie string lines to mark walls, corners and offsets.

Ohm – A designation for electrical resistance.

On Center (OC) – Measuring the distance from the center of one item to the center of another item. For example studs are spaced at either 16"oc or 24"oc.

On Grade – A field term used to communicate that the ground or an assembly is at the desired level.

One Hour Rating – A term used to measure how long it takes for a product or substance to fail or burn when exposed to fire. For example 5/8 sheetrock has a one hour rating.

One Piece Toilet – A toilet where the tank and bowl were manufactured as one complete unit.

Open Bid – When a contractor presents a bid but asks for the right to reduce his bid to compete with a lower bid.

Open Construction – When a phase of an assembly is left unfinished to allow for easy access by an inspector. For example, not starting the insulation until the rough in electrical inspection is complete. Our electrical inspector will fail you automatically if one piece of insulation is up before his rough-in inspection.

Open Excavation – An excavation where nothing is being used to hold back the soils from collapsing in on the dig. It is allowable only with a sufficient angle of repose. (See angle of repose).

Open Plan – A house plan with a lot of open space. An open plan has relatively few interior walls, promoting more interaction with the occupants.

Open Plumbing – Plumbing that is not covered up by a ceiling below. Typically the first floor plumbing is open so it can be accessed from the basement in case of leaks.

Open Roof – A roof where all the structural members are exposed because the floor underneath has no ceiling. Open roofs are most often associated with heavy timber construction, like in log homes.

Operating Transom – A window over a door that opens and closes.

Operable Window – A window that opens and closes.

Operating Expenses – The expenses that are related directly to operations and are variable depending on activity. OEs are also referred to as variable expenses.

Operating Expense Ratio – The ratio between operating expense and revenues.

Orange Peel – A premium finish on drywall that resembles the texture of an orange peel.

Orientation – Refers to the direction the front of the house is facing. Typically east, west, north, or south but can also mean the orientation in relation to a street or road.

Oriented Strand Board (OSB) – A 4'x 8' "plywood like" sheet manufactured by using strands and pieces of wood glued together to make a strong panel. Most often used for wall sheathing and roof sheathing. Advantech® is a good example of a very high quality OSB.

Out of Plumb – Not perfectly vertical or vertically unleveled.

Out of Sequence – Refers to work done earlier or later than scheduled. A good example is one that I referred to earlier where some contractors install wood flooring when messy work is still to be done.

Out of True – A board, beam or other structural member that is twisted or cupped excessively.

Outcrop – An underground rock formation that partially protrudes above grade. Multiple outcroppings are an indicator of possible rock problems.

Over Dig – The extra soil removed past the boundaries of a foundation to make room for working behind a wall safely.

Overflow – For our purposes, a small tank mounted to the outside of a water heater to capture water overflowing the tank thus preventing flooding. Have your plumber install one of these in your home.

Overhead – Expenses that are part of any project but are not directly related to the construction activities. In other words, overhead costs are expenses other than material, labor and equipment.

Overhead Door – A garage door that opens up.

Overhead Service – Electrical service from the power company transmitted to a house by lines located above ground or overhead.

Overload Capacity – The maximum amount of excess power that an electrical appliance or circuit can handle without suffering serious damage.

Oversize Brick – Any brick that is bigger than 2 1/2 "x 3 1/2 "x 7 1/2" which is the size of standard brick.

Owner's Equity – The difference between the values of any asset minus any amount owed on that asset.

Owners Liability Insurance – An insurance policy that protects the property owner in case of an accident on the property. It's a good idea to either carry a separate policy or at least be sure the builder's policy names you as an additional insured. I recommend both.

(P)

Paint Grade – A piece of trim, like base molding, that's not high enough quality to stain but will look fine with paint.

Palladian Window – A three window configuration with one much larger central window and 2 narrower windows on each side.

Pan Construction – Concrete construction using overlapping ribbed metal decking to pour a concrete slab above grade. After years of backfilling elevated porches we started using these and I realized what a dummy I had been. This is the only way to go when pouring concrete over an empty space.

Pane – The glass installed in a window or door, also called lights.

Panel Construction – A framing method where walls are built offsite and assembled onsite together. PC is also referred to as panelized construction.

Panel Door – A door constructed with decorative panels. A common panel door is the six panel door used in many houses.

Panel Strip – A thin piece of material used to hide the joint formed when two pieces of panelized products, like plywood for example, are placed together.

Paraline Drawings – Three-dimensional drawings.

Parallel – When 2 lines or planes are the same distance apart at each and every point.

Parallel Activities – When 2 or more trades can be working at the same time. For example, the electrician, plumber and HVAC contractor can do their "rough-ins" at the same time.

Parapet – A wall section that extends above the roof line.

Parge Coat – A coat of masonry mud on the outside of a block wall to help stop moisture penetration. We have done parge coating on masonry mainly as a stucco application to make exposed masonry look better.

Parquet Flooring – Flooring using small wood squares that form a design pattern.

Particulate Pollution – Pollution made up of tiny floating particles in air and water. Particulates can be very harmful.

Partition – A non-load bearing wall separating areas on the inside of a building.

Pass Through Clause – A clause in a contract allowing a builder to pass part of the responsibilities on to sub-contractors.

Patent Defect – A defect in workmanship or material that can easily be seen with inspection.

Pattern Cracking – Small cracking in a concrete slab in a pattern or shape. Pattern cracking is normally caused by the material settling low in the pour.

Payment Request - A formal written request from the contractor to the owner.

Payment Schedule –See draw schedule.

Payments Withheld- A clause in the general conditions area of the contract explaining under what conditions payments can be withheld from the contractor.

Pedestal Floor – A floor elevated over the subfloor to accommodate pipes or a heating system etc.

Pediment – A non-window decorative piece of material that is installed over an exterior door.

Penalty and Bonus Clause – A contract clause laying out a monetary penalty for a contractor's failure to complete a project or phase by a certain date and allows for a bonus if finished early.

Penal Bond – A bond that combines a performance bond and a labor and materials bond. A penal bond insures that the project is completed and all the bills are paid.

Percent Complete – A method of determining how much of a project is complete as of a certain date. Percent complete is how most contracts are paid for. The contractor or sub gets to a certain phase and is paid for all the work done to that point less any retainage.

Percentage Agreement – A contract where payment is based on a certain percentage of the costs.

Percolation Test (Perc. Test) - A test performed by a soil scientist that rates how well soil will absorb waste water. Perc.testing is very important if you are considering a septic system.

Perennial – A plant with a life cycle of 2 years or more.

Perforated Drain – An underground drain system using a pipe with holes or slits and is covered in gravel. This drain is designed to carry water away form an area. Its main use for house building is to drain water away from the foundation.

Performance – Means to fulfill the terms of the contract for compensation.

Performance Bond – An insurance policy purchased by the builder, guaranteeing the contract will be completed as promised.

Performance Specification – A specification in a contract requiring that some or all work and products meet a certain pre-set criteria or standard.

Performance Based Fee – A method of payment where compensation is based on certain requirements or goals.

Perimeter Drain – The perforated drain system that carries water away from the foundation.

Periphery Wall – A wall on the outside of a building.

Perlite – A lightweight aggregate used in concrete when weight is a consideration.

Permafrost – Permanently frozen ground.

Permanent Load – A load that is a permanent part of the structure, like the weight of the building itself (dead load).

Permeability – The ability of a material or product to allow water vapor to pass through it.

Perspective Drawing – A three dimensional overview drawing of a project.

Pessimistic Time Estimate – The maximum amount of time a task will take to complete. It's very unlikely that it will not be done by this time or date.

Phase – A major part or time period of the construction process. For example the foundation is a phase as is framing etc.

Physical Progress – The measurement of work accomplished in relation to the contract.

Plano Hinge - A hinge that is made with strips across the entire length of the hinge.

Pilaster – A column built inside a wall.

Piling or Pile – A cylinder shaped object driven in the ground to carry a load in unstable soil.

Pile Driver – A big machine for driving piles.

Pitch – The slope on a roof measured in fractions. For example, a roof with a 6/12 pitch or 6 in 12 pitch means that the roof height drops 6 inches vertically for every 12 inches in horizontal length.

Pivoted Door – A door that swings on pivots instead of hinges.

Pivot Window – A window with a sash that operates on a pivot.

Plan View – Means viewed from above.

Plane – Means a flat surface.

Plane Surveying – Surveying small areas, like a home's foundation, and ignoring the curvature of the earth.

Planed Lumber – Lumber that has been run through a planer and is finished on at least one side.

Plasticity – A substance that's pliable enough to be molded into a shape.

Plasticizer – An additive used to increase the plasticity of a building material like concrete or drywall mud.

Plastic Cracking – Cracking in fresh concrete that has not started setting up yet.

Plastic Deformation – A material that has been deformed by a force but doesn't bounce back when the force is removed, like the cupping of lumber.

Plastic Limit – The water content ratio where a soil will begin to crumble.

Plastic Lumber – Another name for the new types of wood made from composites of wood, plastic or recycled materials, used a lot in modern decking.

Plastic Soils – Soils that can be molded without crumbling, like clay.

Plate Glass – A very thick window glass used for large unobstructed windows like storefronts.

Platform Framing – How most houses in the U.S. are built, where each floor is a platform for the next floor.

Plexiglass – The brand name for the most common type of thick glass made of plastic.

Plumbing Stack – A plumbing vent that extends through the roof.

Plumbing Waste Line – A non-pressure rated pipe used to remove sewage.

Plywood - A flat 4'x8' sheet made of thin sheets or plys of wood in which each ply's grain runs opposite of the previous one.

Plywood Grade – A quality rating system for hardwood, designated A through D with A being the highest quality (finished on both sides). Grade also designates how well the product holds up to weather exposure.

Prefabricated Construction – See modular construction

Prefinished – Any construction material finished at the factory, like a prefinished hardwood floor.

Pre-hung Door – A door package where the door slab is already hung on the frame with the hinges in place. It is mortised for the doorknob and has all the hardware.

Preliminary Estimate - An educated guess before an estimate is started. A pre-estimate doesn't mean anything and is best avoided by everyone. I learned to never give a PE.

Preliminary Site Assessment – Typically the first meeting, held at the owners building site, between the owner and contractors wishing to make a bid. It is important because it gives the builder an opportunity to see how the plan will work on the site thus making his estimate much more accurate.

Pump Mix – A concrete mix formulated to pass through a pump.

Punch List –A list of items provided to the contractor by the owner or architect showing what items need to be finished or corrected before closing.

Pyramid Roof –A roof with four sides all meeting at the top (see hip roof).

(Q)

Qualification Submittals – A package prepared by a bidder listing information showcasing their qualifications. Includes things like letters of recommendation, pictures of past work, licenses, proof of insurance etc.

Qualifications and Assumptions – Items that are not 100% clear in the plans or specs that the estimator must use his own judgment and experience to work out.

Quality Acceptance Criteria – A list of the criteria that will be used to decide if a product or task is acceptable.

Quantity Takeoff – The procedure of examining the plans to determine necessary materials and their quantities for a project.

Quarter Round – A molding shaped like 1/4 of a circle used for base shoe and some corner moldings.

Queen Anne Arch – An arch over a palladium window.

Queen Size Brick – An oversize brick that measures 2 3/4" x 3" x 10". I really like the look.

Quick Condition – A situation where small channels have formed in soils from water runoff, significantly reducing the bearing capacity of the soil.

Quitclaim Deed – A deed transferring property.

Quoin – A decorative pattern of brick at a corner where several courses (5-7) of brick are offset in the corner only, and the pattern is repeated several times in the corner.

(R)

R-Value – A material's ability to block heat flow. The higher the R-Value the better the barrier to heat flow.

Radiant Heating and Cooling – Cooling by running cold water through piping and heating by running hot water through piping. Think about the radiators in old classrooms.

Rafter – A sloping board that runs parallel to several like members, all holding up the roof decking.

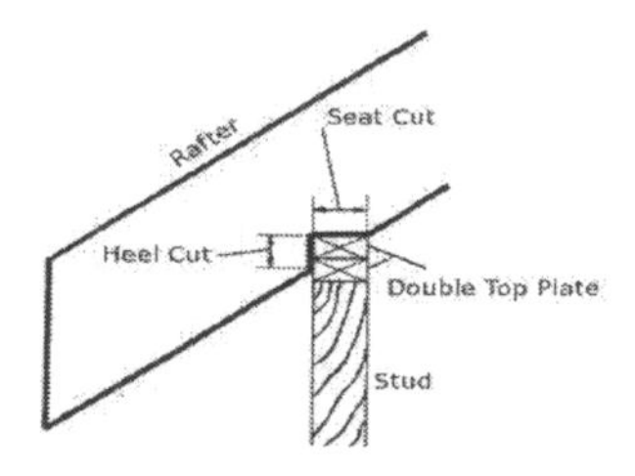

Rapid Hardening Cement – Commonly called high early cement, it is cement that strengthens at a faster pace than standard concrete.

Rapidly Renewable Materials – Raw materials like bamboo that can be grown very quickly making them a green alternative.

Ready Mix Concrete – Concrete that is delivered in a concrete truck in a workable state.

Real Property – Land and anything on it.

Reasonable Care and Skill – A legal term that defines the levels of performance that can be expected in a trade or area of expertise. Basically says if a builder calls himself a builder he should know what he is doing.

Rebar –Short for reinforcing bar.

Reclaimed Lumber – Wood that's been removed from an old building and is still in good enough condition to be reused.

Record Drawings – Also called "as built drawings". These are updated drawings that show any changes and copies are provided to local building officials for their files.

Record Sheet or Log – A written record of events on a construction site.

Recording Fee – Money paid to the local Registrar of Deeds for keeping a record of a deed.

Red Herring –A negotiation term for a tactic where one party makes a proposal specifically to distract the other party.

Redlline – Making a change on a drawing with a pencil.

Redress –Financial compensation to one party for damages caused by another.

Reference Line – A line or series of points used as a reference from which to pull measurements.

Reference Standard – A product or substance referenced in the specifications to compare products to set standards. For example, it may state owner wants product A to perform at least as well as product B.

Reinforcing Bar (Rebar) – A steel bar with equally spaced ridges that is used to give concrete much more strength. Rebar comes in different diameters depending on its use.

Reinforced Concrete – Concrete made stronger with the use of steel.

Reinforced Masonry – Concrete masonry block with steel rebar and concrete filling the cavities.

Related Trades – The many different building trades required to complete a specific project.

Relative Compaction – A measurement of the dry density of a soil sample.

Release of Lien – The written document formally canceling a lien.

Remediation – The process of correcting a health hazard like mold removal.

Remedies – Actions a court uses to correct a contract violation.

Rendering – An unscaled representation of a project or part of a project used to give someone a general idea what the finished project will look like. A rendering often uses shading and shadows for emphasis.

Replacement Cost – The cost to replace a structure at the current cost of construction.

Replacement Cost Coverage – An insurance policy that replaces a loss at the current cost without depreciation. I recommend these policies.

Requisition – A formal application for payment for work completed. Requisition is another term for draw request.

Residual Approach – A method for determining the cost of an assembly or phase on a construction site.

Respondent – The defendant in a construction claim.

Responsiveness – A measure of how well a bid conforms to the requirements of the bidding documents.

Restitution – A court ordered reimbursement for monetary damages.

Restrictive Covenant – A rule stated within a deed restricting, in some way, what a piece of real property can be used for.

Retainage – A contracted portion of each draw request that is held by the owner until the project is completed.

Retaining Wall – A sturdy wall built to hold back the earth behind it.

Retarder – An additive in concrete meant to slow down the setup process. Retarder is used on a real hot day to keep the concrete from getting hard before it can be placed.

Re-tempering - The addition of water to a concrete mix to increase its workability. A little is ok but too much can really hurt the finished strength.

Retention (see retainage) **–** Retainage expressed as a percentage of a draw request.

Reticulated – In a grid or set up with crossing lines. On my sites we use the word for a rebar grid where rebar is set in a parallel and perpendicular grid to strengthen a slab.

Retrofit – The process of upgrading an existing building or assembly.

Return Air Vent – A vented opening through which air is recirculated back into an HVAC system.

Reveal – The small openings around a window or door.

Reverberation – An echo.

Reverse Swing Door – A door that opens from the inside of a room outward.

Rich Mix – A concrete or mortar mix with a high percentage of Portland cement.

Ridge – The horizontal line forming at the top of a roof where the two slopes meet.

Ridge Vent – A vent running along the ridge of a roof that gives hot air a way to escape from an attic. When used with vented soffit, it is the most efficient way to ventilate an attic.

Rim Joist – The joist at the buildings perimeter that runs perpendicular to the common joists.

Ring-Shank Nail – A nail with ring shaped ridges along its body that make it grip better. This is the only nail we use.

Rip Rap – Large rock between the size of a softball to the size of a basketball with irregular surfaces. It is used in ditches and other places to prevent erosion. Rip Rap is very effective in stopping erosion.

Rise and Run – The slope of a roof expressed as a fraction or ratio. For example, 6/12 means a roof rises 6" for every 12" it runs outward. Rise and run is also used to layout stairs.

Riser – The vertical board between two stair treads.

Riser Height – The vertical distance from the top of one stair tread to the top of the next tread.

Roman Brick – A brick that measures 4" x 2" x 12".

Rough Estimate – A WAG or wild ass guess.

Rough Grading – The excavation that gets the general shape of the grade; before finished grade.

Rough Opening – The opening that a door or window frame will fit into. RO is normally about 1/2" bigger than the window or door itself. For example if you purchased a 36" door the RO would be 36 1/2.

Rough In – The installation of the hidden part of electrical, plumbing and HVAC systems.

Rowlock Course – The brick laying method used to finish exterior window sills. Each brick is laid on its edge, pointing from inside to out with the end of the brick facing out. A rowlock slopes down slightly to shed water away from the window.

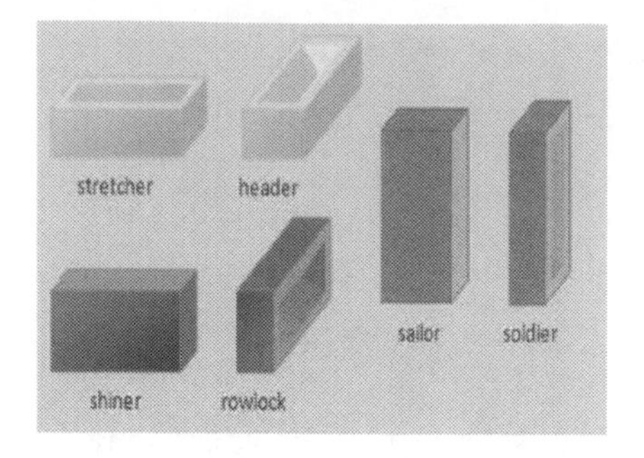

Running Foot – A name often used in the field meaning linear foot or lengthways.

Run Off – Rain water that flows away from a site as opposed to standing and soaking in.

(S)

Sacking – A method of fixing a concrete surface by mixing cement, sand and water and rubbing the paste over rough spots with a piece of burlap.

Safety Factor – Means a little extra. In engineering, if a beam is meant to support 6000 lbs. it might be designed to support 6500 lbs. with the extra 500 lbs. being the safety factor. In estimating, let's figure a house will cost $200,000. We should estimate $220,000 for a 10% safety factor.

Safety Glass – Also called tempered glass or laminated glass. A type of glass manufactured to shatter into very small pieces instead of large sheets that could cause life threatening injuries.

Safety Shutoff – A device in a gas appliance designed to shut off the supply of gas if the flame goes out.

Sanded Grout – Grout used to fill in joints between tiles that have sand in the mix.

Sanding Sealer – A clear coat sealer applied to wood, sealing the woods pores, before the finish stain is applied to prevent the wood from soaking up the stain. Good stuff!

Sanitary Sewage – All the waste carried away from a house generated from the bathroom and waste pipes. Sewage does not include storm water.

Sanitary Sewer – Any piping that carries sanitary sewage for treatment.

Sash – The framework in a window that holds the glass in place. A sash may be operating or non-operating.

Satisfaction – The release or cancellation of a lien or hold on a piece of property.

Sawzall – A slang or field name for a reciprocating saw.

Scaled Drawing – A plan drawing in which all the dimensions are reduced down to a scale model. For example most house plans are drawn at 1/4" equals one foot. So every 1/4 inch of line drawn on the plan represents one foot of actual construction.

Schedule Compression – Basically putting off a bunch of little insignificant tasks until they become a major issue and must be completed before the project can move forward.

Schedule Contingency – Extra time or a safety factor built into a job schedule to allow for unexpected issues.

Schematic Design – A breakdown of the design into its separate phases.

Scissor Truss – A truss that has a sloping bottom chord and is used to provide extra space for a cathedral ceiling.

Sconce – A wall mounted light fixture.

Scope – A summary of the entire project.

Scope of Work – A very detailed description of a task to be performed by a contractor, sub-contractor or supplier.

Scrap Out – Cleaning up after drywall is hung. This should be included in the hanger's price.

Scratch Coat – The first coat of drywall mud or stucco.

Screed – The rough leveling of concrete as it is placed.

Sealer – Any liquid used to fill in the pores on a surface. For our purposes it is wood sealer, like sanding sealer, to seal the wood's pores before staining or a sealer that should be applied to concrete within 24 hours of the placement. Concrete sealer is called cure and seal.

Secondary Financing – A loan secured by a second mortgage that is subordinate to the first mortgage.

Secondary Sub-Contractor – Any sub-contractor not listed as a prime contractor. For example a subcontractor hired by the electrical sub to clean up when he is finished with his rough in.

Sequence of Operation – The order of the work or phases to be completed in a project.

Settlement – The total amount the insured and the insurance company agree to settle a claim for. Also is a depression that develops in soils after the finished grade.

Sewage Gases – Vapors or odors emitted from raw sewage or a sewage system. The homeowner should not come into contact with these odors unless the wax seal on the toilet is not seated correctly or the septic systems field lines have failed.

Shear Forces – Forces acting diagonally or laterally on a structure or a component of that structure.

Shear Failure – The point where shearing forces cause a failure in a construction component, an assembly or a failure in a soil. Shear failure is a diagonally sliding failure.

Shear Slide – A land slide where the top soil moves away from the soil beneath it in a large, single mass.

Sheathing Felt – A roofing felt that is placed between the roof decking and the shingles.

Shed Roof – A roof with a single sloping deck or plane.

Shrinkage – Volume or size reduction caused by drying in concrete and wood. It is part of the curing process in concrete and is not a problem unless excessive. Wood naturally expands and contracts. Shrinkage is not a problem unless it is excessive.

Siding – Any material meant to be the finished exterior covering for a wall.

Silica – Silicon dioxide. Breathing the dust from silica can be a major health hazard. Breathing protection should always be worn when cutting any product containing silica.

Single Hung Window – A window with two sashes, one on top of the other where the bottom sash operates and the top sash is fixed.

Site – The location where the construction project is taking place.

Site Audit – An inspection and review of the construction project examining the accuracy of what has been reported compared to what has actually happened on the site.

Site Built – Site built means the entire project is assembled on the site where it will remain as opposed to having some parts assembled offsite as in modular or prefabbed construction.

Site Investigation – The detailed examination of all the surface and sub-surface conditions on a building site.

Site Plan – A drawing representing the entire area where the work is being done including the outline of the building, parking, driveways, sidewalks, landscaping and the boundaries.

Slab – A horizontal placement of concrete that follows the contour of the ground under it and sits on the ground. It can be a floor or foundation for a building (flat top) or can be a driveway or sidewalk slab which follows the contour (flatwork).

Slump – Measures the consistency of a concrete mix. Slump is measured by placing some of the concrete mix in a cone shaped mold and then turning the cone over. The distance the height decreases when the cone mold is removed is the slump of the concrete mix.

Smart Landscaping – A landscaping plan that is limited to plants and shrubs that do well without much water, fertilizer or pesticides.

Soffit –The underside of the eave and the building material that covers this area from the exterior wall to the bottom of the fascia board.

Soil Classification Testing – A series of tests designed to grade and classify soils.

Soil Structure – The microscopic pattern that soils are arranged in.

Solar Gain – The free heat from the sun that travels through the glass in windows and doors.

Solar Orientation – The positioning of a building to take advantage of the suns position in the sky. Colder climates in the northern hemisphere benefit from a southern exposure and the warmer climates would benefit from a northern exposure.

Solarium – A room with lots of glass and an orientation to take advantage of the sun.

Soldier Course – A course of brick with each brick standing on its end and the narrow edge facing out.

Solid Brick – A brick without holes and solid all the way through.

Solid Core Door – A door mostly used for entry doors or fire doors that are solid all the way through. These are more expensive but I used them on every door in my house. If you can afford it, I suggest you do the same.

Solid Wall – A wall made of solid concrete.

Special Hazards Insurance – An insurance policy covering hazards that would not normally be included in a liability or property damage policy.

Specifications or Specs – Documents in the contract that lay out specific requirements for quality or brand, for products, materials and workmanship for the project.

Specifier – The person requesting the specs as noted in the specification documents.

Speculative Builder – A contractor who builds a house without a specific buyer. A spec builder purchases a lot and builds the house with the intent of selling it for a profit before he has a buyer lined up. I started as a spec builder and I still love building spec homes.

Splayed Window – Any window set in an angled wall.

Split Face Block – A concrete block with one side that has a rough irregular shape and is made by splitting two blocks apart instead of cutting them smooth.

Split Jamb – A two-piece door jamb that comes on a pre-hung door and made where each piece is installed from opposite sides of the rough opening. Split jambs make it possible for door casings to be installed in the factory.

Spray in Place Insulation – Any insulation like loose cellulose or foam insulation that is applied by a spray or an air blower.

Spread Footing – A footer that is wider than the wall it supports and is designed to spread the load over a larger area of the subgrade.

Square – The way shingles are packaged. A square of shingles will cover 100 square feet of roof.

Stairwell – A vertical shaft that encloses a stairway.

Standard Tolerance – The generally accepted variance in size or quality for a specific type of product or assembly.

Statement of Probable Construction Costs – An architect's estimate of construction costs. It is normally a wild ass guess (WAG) based on figures that have nothing to do with reality.

Static Pressure - The pressure exerted by a liquid that's not moving.

Stringers – The three 2'x 12" boards that support the treads in a stair system.

Structural Drawings – Drawings of the parts, assemblies and systems that support or hold up the building.

Structural Failure – Failure of part or all of the framing system.

Structural Steel – Cold rolled steel specifically designed as structural and load bearing members in a framing system. The most common structural steel is a beam.

Sub- Contractor – A trade contractor that is contracted by the prime contractor to perform the work on a specific part of the project.

Sub-Floor – The rough structural floor supported by the floor joists or trusses that serves as a base for the finish flooring.

Sub-Grade – The level and excavated base ground which a foundation is built on.

Submittal – A sample of a product or a drawing submitted by the contractor or architect to the owner for approval to use in the project.

Subsidence – Basically a large sink hole.

Substantial Completion – The point in the construction where the project is complete enough to be used for its intended purpose but, not necessarily 100% complete.

Substrate – Any material that supports another material. For example the compacted soil is a substrate of the concrete footing.

Subsurface Contamination – Contamination of the ground under a site from chemicals, sewage or some other contaminate.

Supplemental Agreement – A change or addition to the contract that's agreed to by both parties.

Surety – Any company that provides a bond guaranteeing that a contractor will perform according to the contract.

Suspension of Work Notice – A notice given to the contractor by the owner or a governmental agency forcing work on the project to stop.

Sustainable Design – A design method that takes into consideration the reduction of the use of natural resources like wood.

Swale – A shallow ditch or depression designed to collect and temporarily hold storm water runoff.

Synergy – People, products, materials or substances working together to produce a specific condition or effect.

(T)

Tag Line – A line or rope attached to an item that's being lifted by a crane. A tag line is used to control unwanted side to side movement during the lift.

Take-off – The process of determining materials and products needed and their quantities taken from the plan drawings and spec sheets.

Tangibles – Items that can be counted or measured. Real

Tank-Less Water Heater – A water heating system that doesn't have a holding tank. A tank-less heats water on demand only. These things supposedly save energy but make sure if you buy one you only buy a gas or propane unit because you'll freeze your butt off with an electric.

Target Date – The date that everyone is shooting for in the project. It is either a start date or finish date for a project, task or phase.

Target Price Contract – A cost plus or a fixed sum contract where the owner and contractor agree on a price to shoot for and the contractor does his best to be at or under that price.

Target Schedule – The optimal project schedule that the actual schedule is compared to in order to judge performance.

Task – A detailed individual job within a phase. A phase is made up of multiple well defined tasks.

Task Lighting – Lighting that is necessary to accomplish a specific task.

Tear Off - The first step in replacing a roof. It is the act of tearing off the old roof down to bare decking.

Tempered Glass – A very strong glass used in places like sliding doors and windows less than 12 to 24 inches off the finished floor, depending on the code. TG is not only resistant to shattering but if it does break; it breaks into tiny pieces making it less dangerous.

Tempering – Adding water to a concrete mix at the site and before it leaves the truck. It is done to make the mix more workable and should not be overdone because it affects strength.

Tensile Strength – A materials ability to resist pulling and stretching.

Tension - A pulling or stretching force on a material.

Terminal Expense – An expense incurred by the contractor, the owner or both that must be spent in order to completely finish the contract. An example might be a fee charged by a bank that has to be paid before they will release the final payment.

Termination for Default – The formal act of firing a contractor for an inexcusable failure to live up to the terms of the contract.

Termite Shield – A thin piece of metal placed on top of a foundation wall to prevent termite infestation. These are not necessary if the ground is pre-treated properly.

Terms of Payment – The specific agreement on the timing of and the amount of payments throughout the project.

Tertiary Beam – A beam in a structural system that transfers its load to another beam.

Test Cylinder – A cylinder shaped concrete sample that is taken offsite, put in a machine and crushed to determine the compressive strength of the sample. If a sample is supposed to be 3,500 psi then it should be able to take up to 3,500 lbs. of pressure before breaking.

Test Pit – A small excavation to obtain a sub-surface soil sample to be tested.

Thermal Resistance – A materials ability to resist the transfer of heat.

Third Party Claim – A claim against the contractor, owner or both by an unrelated party, usually for a personal injury or property damage.

Three Way Switch – An electrical switch that controls the same light or appliance from two separate locations.

Threshold – A metal strip that runs between door jambs at the bottom of a door. A threshold is used to keep weather from entering from under an exterior door.

Tieback – A rod tied between a dead man and a retaining wall to prevent the wall from falling over.

Tied Column – A column that is tied to the floor and again at the top to prevent one or the other from moving sideways.

Tight Buildings – A building envelope that's designed to minimize air infiltration thus saving money on heating and cooling. This can be overdone to the point that a building can't breathe.

Tilt Up – A method of building walls where the wall is assembled on the floor and then tilted up into place either by jacks, a crane or several workers.

Time is of the Essence – A clause in a building contract declaring the importance of keeping on schedule.

Time Line – A chart with a line on which important dates, milestones or tasks are shown.

Time of Completion – It is the time period in scheduling allowed for each phase or a date for which a task must be completed.

Time Sensitive Costs – Costs that keep going as long as an activity continues. For example, a crane has been rented and as long as it is on site it's costing money.

Timely Completion – The completion of a phase or task in a time period that conforms to the schedule.

Title – A document proving ownership in an asset.

Title Insurance – An insurance policy guaranteeing that the title for real property is clear.

Title Search – A search of the history of a piece of real property to determine if there are any problems that might cloud the title like liens, restrictions or some other defect.

Ton – A measure of heating and cooling capacity of a HVAC unit equal to 12,000 BTUs per hour. Also is a weight measurement equal to 2,000 lbs.

Tongue and Groove – Lumber, siding or wood flooring that is made with a groove on one side and a matching tongue on the other side; designed to slide together creating a tight fit.

Top Chord – The top part of a truss.

Top Soil –The dark top layer of soil necessary for grass or other plant life to grow. It is the highest quality soil in the mix.

Torque – A rotating force.

Torsion – The twisting of a structural member like a board or beam.

Total Run – The total distance covered by a rafter including any overhang.

Trade – Expertise or skill in a specific type of construction work. Typical trades are carpenters, electricians, plumbers, HVAC techs and brick masons among others.

Trade Discount – A discount from list price offered by suppliers to contractors and trade sub-contractors to promote loyalty. This is one of the reasons you can't really save much money by being your own contractor.

Transit Mix – A concrete mix that is mixed partially in the concrete truck on the way to the job site. This is the way almost all concrete is transported to a job site.

Transition Strip – A strip of metal or wood placed across an opening when transitioning from one type of flooring to another like from tile to carpet.

Transmission Line – A high voltage electric line.

Transom –A piece of glass, either operating or fixed, placed over another window or a door.

Trench Box – A brace built from wood or steel sheathing designed to be moved along a trench to hold back the trench walls from collapsing on workers laying pipe or conduit. Anytime workers are in ditches over 36" high there needs to be either a trench box or an angle of repose sufficient to prevent a collapse from trapping a worker.

Trench Drain – A pre-formed trench made of metal, concrete or plastic, covered with a grate and used to collect water at a low point and drain it away from the area.

Truss – An engineered assembly designed by a licensed structural engineer, built offsite and used in place of joists in floor assemblies and rafters in a roof assembly.

Turnaround Time – The estimated time to perform a process offsite and get it back to the site, ready to use or install.

Two Way Reinforced Footing – A footing with rebar running in two different directions, perpendicular to each other.

Two Way Slab – A slab with rebar running in two directions perpendicular to each other forming a cage usually with 1-2 foot squares. I always build these on any slab that had any filling done unless I am using metal decking.

Tyvek House Wrap® – A great brand name product manufactured by the Dupont Corporation. It's a high quality house wrap that keeps moisture from penetrating walls while still allowing the building to breathe. I really like this stuff. In recent years we have been using the Zip System® from J.M. Huber Corporation, the makers of Advantech® just because it's easier to install properly. In other words it is idiot proof. (Note: In case you are wondering neither Dupont nor J.M. Huber has any idea or care who I am and neither pays me to plug their products. They just make a few advanced products that I really like.)

(U)

U Factor – A measure of a materials heat transmission capability.

Umbrella Policy – An insurance policy that covers losses that may not be covered in other policies; like general liability. Its main benefit is the coverage kicks in after another policies benefit has been exhausted.

Unconscionability – A contract that is so unfair or one sided that it's unenforceable.

Unconsolidated – Un-compacted soil that should be compacted before it's built upon.

Under Protest – Where one party disagrees with an action but in the interest of time allows it to go forward but reserves the right to contest the action or file a claim at a later date.

Under Floor Heating – A heating system that uses electrical wiring or pipes underneath a finished floor to provide a heated finish floor. UFH is popular now in bathrooms.

Underlayment – Plywood or a similar product used on a sub-floor to make a smoother surface for the finish floor.

Uniform Commercial Code – A code guiding most commercial transactions.

Uniform Fire Code – A model code developed by the National Fire Protection Association to protect property and people from fire and explosion.

Un-interruptible Power Supply – A system that is designed to kick in during a power outage. A gas operated generator is a good example.

Unit Cost – The cost of a specific quantity of a product.

Unit Cost Contract – A contract priced per unit of output like per hour, per ton or per piece.

Unlimited Schedule – A construction schedule with no pre-set time constraints.

Unseasoned –Lumber that has not been dried sufficiently.

Unsupported Wall Height – The maximum height a code allows for a masonry wall; determined using the ratio between height and wall thickness. For example a wall built with 12 inch block can be built higher than a wall built with 8 inch block.

Upcharge – A charge for something extra.

Uptime – The amount of time a machine or a worker is actually working as desired.

Utility Easement – An area legally setback from the property line, typically 15-20 feet, where the utility companies place their lines and hookups.

Utility Survey – A map showing utilities that are currently in place on a property or an area around a property.

(V)

Valance –A small board, just above a window, used to hide the working parts of drapery or shutters.

Valley – The areas where two roof lines meet and where water from both runs in a channel.

Valley Flashing – Thin metal lining a valley to prevent water leaks.

Valley Gutter – The open trough in a valley to channel away water.

Value Engineering – Design that compares cost to the total value provided for products and assemblies.

Value of Work Performed – The value of a project or a task after it is completed.

Vandalism Insurance – An insurance policy that specifically covers intentional damage by morons with nothing better to do.

Variable Costs – The costs associated with work. Variable costs are controllable versus fixed costs that are incurred whether work is occurring or not.

Variable Rate – An interest rate that can fluctuate during the life of a loan.

Variance – Permission granted to deviate from a zoning ordinance or rule normally required by a governmental agency.

Veneer – Wood sliced into thin sheets, plywood is made of multiple veneers.

Veranda – A covered porch or balcony.

Verification – Confirming that a product, material or task meets the required specifications.

Visqueen – Thick and durable plastic sheeting.

(W)

W-Truss – A wooden truss with the structural web resembling a w.

Wainscot – The bottom part of a wall, usually separated by chair rail, which is decorated differently than the top. The most common wainscot is defined with wood trim or panels but is often defined by two distinct paint colors.

Waiver of Lien – A document in which a person or company holding the possible right to place a mechanics lien, acknowledges having been paid either partially or in full and releases their lien rights for the amount paid.

Wall Tie – A metal strip with curved edges used to tie brick to a wall.

Warranty Deed – A deed transferring real property in which the grantor guarantees that the title is clear.

Water Bar – A metal strip on the exterior window sill designed to stop water infiltration.

Water Closet – The official name for a modern toilet that stores its flush water.

Water Hammer – A loud banging noise in water pipes that occurs when water is abruptly shut off. The sudden shut off of flow causes a shock wave that creates the loud banging noise.

Water Main – A main supply line in a public water system.

Water Tap – A valve that taps into a public water main.

Water Table – The highest level of groundwater in an area.

Water – Cement Ratio – A measure of the amount of water compared to the amount of cement expressed as a fraction or a decimal. This ratio is important because if the percentage of water is too high the concrete's strength will suffer.

Weathered – Designed to shed water or the face of an old builder.

Weather-strip – A piece of material placed at openings around the edges of windows and doors, designed to keep out weather and air infiltration.

Web – The center part of a beam or truss between the top and bottom chords that carry the loads.

Weep Hole – A hole in a masonry wall, placed near the bottom to provide a way for moisture to escape the area behind the wall. You should always have weep holes in a brick wall or a retaining wall.

Weir – A gateway in a channel, ditch or gutter designed to divert water.

Weld – The joining of two pieces of metal with sufficient heat to melt them together.

Welded Truss – A metal truss with the parts joined together by welding.

Welded Wire Fabric Reinforcement – Thin metal wire matting used as reinforcement in concrete to help prevent cracking. WWF is old school and ineffective compared to using fiber in concrete. I always hated it. If it's not placed properly it is worthless.

Welt – A seam in metal roofing connecting two sheets by folding the edges over each other and then flattening out the folded seam.

Wet Mix – A concrete mix containing too much water.

Wind Load – The lateral wind force a structure is designed to withstand.

Wind Uplift – The upward force produced when wind travels around or over a structure. This is the force that tears the roofs of buildings in a hurricane or tornado.

Wind Break – Trees or structures placed strategically to protect the building or an area from wind.

Window Schedule – A section or page of the drawings listing all the windows by type, size, color and hardware requirements.

Window Treatments – Window coverings like blinds, curtains etc.

Window Well – A wall or form protecting a below grade window. Below grade windows are typically in basements.

Withe – A partition separating two flues in a chimney.

Wood – Frame Construction – A framing system where the floors, walls, roof and structural members are all made of wood.

Work – All the labor, materials and equipment used to complete the project in accordance with the contract documents.

Work Capacity – The biggest job a contractor or sub-contractor can handle without increasing fixed costs or hiring more people.

Workers Compensation Insurance – A state required insurance that provides for the medical care and loss of wages for an employee hurt while on the job. I can't stress enough how important this is.

Workmanship – The quality of work completed. Workmanship can be of good quality or poor quality.

Wrecking – A nickname for demolishing an assembly or an entire structure.

(X)

X – Brace – A brace shaped like an X that is placed between joists or floor trusses to prevent them from turning over.

XCU – An insurance policy; stands for specific items excluded or not covered.

(Y)

Yard – A volume measurement for concrete that is equal to a cubic yard 3′ x 3′ x 3′ or 27 cubic feet. In carpeting it's equal to one square yard, 3′ x 3′ or 9 square feet.

Yard Lumber – Lumber from a lumber yard that has been graded by size, length and type.

(Z)

Zero Lot Line – Multi-family housing connected together and placed on multiple individual lots.

Zoned Control – The separation of areas in a home to have better control over heating and cooling. For example modern HVAC systems can be set for one temperature in a master suite and a different temperature for a bedroom that is rarely used.

Zoning – The control of land use by a governmental agency like the local planning commission. A planning commission will separate areas of a city or county for use as housing, industrial, retail, and multi-family residential to prevent for example a factory next to a residential development.

References

Chapter 2

Value Engineering. (2014, December 24). In *Wikipedia, T*
he Free Encyclopedia. Retrieved 17:57, December 29, 2014,

http://en.wikipedia.org/w/index.php?title=Value_engineeri ng&oldid=639513793

Chapter 3

Very Funny Jokes. (2007, November 7). Really Funny Jokes - Building Contractor. Retrieved from http://miteshasher.blogspot.com/2007/11/really-funny-jokes-building-contractor.html

Chapter 4

Harris, C. M. (2013). *McGraw-Hill Dictionary of Architecture and Construction.* New York, NY: McGraw-Hill Companies, Inc.

Chapter 7

Birds Mouth Joint. (2015, January 15). In Wikipedia, The Free Encyclopedia
Retrieved: 15 January 2015
http://en.wikipedia.org/wiki/Birdsmouth_joint

Dimensional Shingle. (2015, January 15) Canstock stock photo. http://www.canstockphoto.com/images-photos/asphalt-roof.html#file_view.php?id=15334240

English Bond and Flemish Bond. (2015, January 15). In Wikipedia, The Free Encyclopedia. Retrieved: 15 January 2015
http://en.wikipedia.org/wiki/Brickwork

Hip Roof. (2015, January 15). In Wikipedia, The Free Encyclopedia.
Retrieved: 15 January 2015
http://en.wikipedia.org/w/index.php?title=Hip_roof&oldid=635807021

I-Joist. (2015, January 15). In Wikipedia, The Free Encyclopedia.
Retrieved: 15 January 2015
http://en.wikipedia.org/wiki/I-joist

www.chubbybuilder.com

chubby@chubbybuilder.com

situation. You should seek the services of a competent professional before beginning any improvement program. The story and its characters and entities are fictional. Any likeness to actual persons, either living or dead, is strictly coincidental.

Acknowledgments:

To my wife April and my grand-kids, Chase and Lacey, thank you for your love and patience. To Doctor Julie, thank you for your editing work, yours and Rod's friendship, my nickname and your significant contribution to the quality of this project.